BRIDE PRICE

Ian Mathie spent his childhood in Africa and returned there, after school and a short service commission in the RAF, as a rural development officer for the British government. His work in water resources and related projects during the 1970s brought him in close contact with the African people and their rich cultures and varied tribal customs, many of which are now all but lost. These experiences were the inspiration for four African memoirs, one of which is *Bride Price*. Ian continued to visit Africa until health considerations curtailed his travelling. He now lives in Warwickshire with his wife and dog.

By the same author

African Memoir Series:
Man in a Mud Hut
Supper with the President
The Man of Passage

Keep Taking the Pills

BRIDE PRICE

Ian Mathie

MOSAÏQUEPRESS

Published by

MOSAÏQUE PRESS

Registered office:
70 Priory Road
Kenilworth, Warwickshire CV8 1LQ
www.mosaïquepress.co.uk

Cover design by Gary Henderson
GH Graphic Design Ltd

Printed in the UK.

ISBN 978-1-906852-08-5

For Abélé and Nina,
two daughters for whom
I set their bride price.

List of illustrations

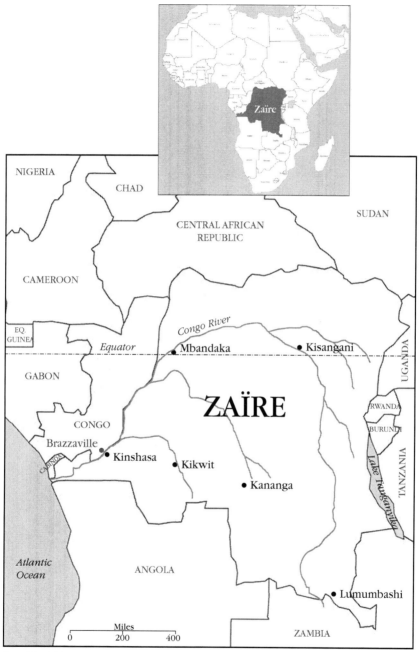

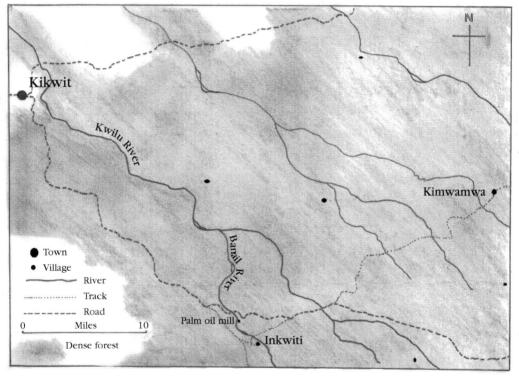

The forested Kikwit district of Zaïre's Bandundu province.

Introduction

IT IS COMMON FOR MEN in Africa to pay a bride price to their prospective bride's father when they choose to marry. This usually involves some exchange of goods or livestock and is entangled with all sorts of complicated rituals, symbolism and taboos. The significance of the bride price often reaches well beyond the central characters in the deal; it may commit people in both extended families to enduring obligations and responsibilities and result in debts that can often take years, even generations, to pay off. In some societies, the bride price is always negotiated by intermediaries acting on behalf of the man and his family. In other cultures, the man must negotiate the bride price himself, directly with the girl's father or guardian.

In addition to the economic exchange, which is, in part, compensation to the bride's family for the loss of one of the principal workers of their household, the manner in which the bride price is paid is often important. This demonstrates the value a prospective husband places on his bride and cements bonds of loyalty between the two families. It also demonstrates the respect he has for the bride's father who will, at the time of the marriage, become his father. The bride price thus has many facets including the basic economic exchange, the establishment of a bond of commitment between the families and the public acknowledgement of the social status of all the parties involved. This is a particularly important aspect for it sets a benchmark for the bride's status in the community and that of the children she bears.

The mechanisms for setting, negotiating and paying the bride price vary extensively across the continent, as do the penalties incurred if the marriage should fail and the bride be rejected or returned. The consequences are invariably surrounded by many complex customs that are but dimly understood by people from outside the group where the agreements were negotiated and the deal was struck.

I went to West Africa as a rural development officer in 1970 and soon found myself specialising in water resources. Over the years I travelled to many other regions. An assignment in 1975 took me to Zaïre, during the rule of President Mobutu, to work on a project developing clean spring water supplies among isolated forest communities. The project was located in the dense jungle region of Bandundu province, to the south-east of Kikwit and about 450 kilometres from the capital, Kinshasa.

Commuting from the town proved impractical and I found it preferable to live in a small forest village, among the people with whom I was working. The sector political officer helped me find a suitable home in a village called Inkwiti where, through a combination of convoluted circumstances, I found myself fostering an orphan girl of thirteen and a half. Although she was part of the community, she had become ostracised through no fault of her own and needed a home and a guardian in order to restore her status and give her some future prospects. Since she had reached puberty and was, according to local tradition, of marriageable age, it became my responsibility to set the bride price when a man arrived one day and asked for her hand in marriage.

The problem was that the man who asked to marry her was most unsuitable and unacceptable as a suitor. He made it obvious that he despised me and the villagers among whom I lived, so what might have been just a complicated puzzle with a rational solution now took on a whole new dimension of intrigue and political manoeuvring.

This is the true story of how the problem was resolved.

AUTHOR'S NOTES

A few African words are used in the text because they do not translate simply into English. These are explained in the Glossary: see page 232.

The quality of some of the photographs and sketches are indicative of the era, conditions in rural Zaïre and general handling of camera, film and paper. They are included for their general interest and historic value.

The village of Inkwiti. The author's house is at the top of the map.

Chapter 1

THE AIR WAS STAGNANT and oppressive in the late tropical afternoon as I sat cross-legged on the floor of my hut, trying to restore life to a battered Tilley lamp. My thoughts rambled freely over a range of recent village events, while my fingers cleaned and repaired the pieces. The soft clapping of hands outside the open door announced the arrival of a visitor.

"My house is open," I called. "Enter and be welcome."

A dark shadow filled the doorway, briefly blackening the already dim room, as a huge man stooped and entered.

"Your house is cool and I am pleased to find you," the visitor intoned softly, "Greetings." His manner was formal as befits one who is a stranger to the house and its owner.

The man moved fully into the room as I looked up to inspect my unexpected visitor.

"Your visit is welcome," I said formally, rising.

Following the custom of the greeting I motioned him towards the only chair. This was a rickety cane structure which I found uncomfortable and seldom used myself, but it had been given to me by the village headman when I first came here, so I kept it. The chair creaked in protest as the giant lowered himself into it and looked around the room.

My house consisted of only the one room. Compared to many others in the village it was quite large, about sixteen feet square, with mud walls and a thatched roof. The inside still showed the remains of some whitewash that had been applied long ago and badly needed repainting. I would do it one day. The shutters on the single window were open and hung slightly askew where the hinges had sagged. At some time in the distant past the shutters had been given a coat of green paint, but this too was now faded as time and the damp heat of the forest had taken their toll. Irregular poles cut from the stems of thin forest saplings, most of them still wearing their bark, were bound together with vines and overlaid with coarse grass matting that formed the foundation of the steep, newly thatched roof. The eaves were broad and low to prevent the tropical rain from eating away at the walls. Despite the stagnant air outside a cool current of air crept through between the top of the walls and the underside of the thatch.

My visitor's eyes swept the room slowly with the intensity of an electron microscope, and missed nothing. There was a bamboo bed in one corner covered with a piece of locally dyed cloth, two carved wooden stools from one of the northern provinces and a small table with one broken leg which was splinted and bound with raffia. A faded curtain hung from a pole across the rear corner, fresh grass mats partially covered the beaten clay floor, and finally there was me, surrounded by a clutter of assorted tools and lamp parts.

Outside the door, against the wall and sheltered by the eaves, I had buried two large earthen pots with only their thick rims showing above the ground. They had tightly fitting wooden covers and kept the drinking water inside them cool. I took a small plastic jug from its place in the rafters above the door, filled it from one of the pots and placed it on the table beside my visitor. Behind the curtain in the back corner stood a basket filled with fruit which had been collected in the forest that morning. I chose the four best pieces and placed them in a smaller basket. Then, taking a clean glass from the shelf, I returned to my visitor.

He was staring intently out of the doorway, his attention fixed on something outside.

"The food is poor," I said placing it with the glass on the table.

The big man drew his attention back into the room, glancing first at me, then at the table.

"The food is good. You honour me," he said, in a slightly offhand manner but completing the sequence of the greeting.

For a few moments more he looked at me without expression then reached out and selected a mango from the basket. With no attempt to remove the leathery skin he bit into it savagely, squirting a brief fountain of juice which subsided to dribble down his round chin and drip onto the front of his shirt. With sluppering, sucking noises he consumed the fruit as if he had not eaten for days.

His presence completely dominated the room. I felt a faint tremor of apprehension and began, for the first time I could remember, to feel uncomfortable in my own home.

The afternoon light was dim inside the house but there was enough to let me see the man clearly and to examine his features and huge frame. By the way he had stooped to enter I judged that he must be well over six feet tall and he was massively built. I wondered if he came from one of the south-eastern provinces of the country, where many of the men were this tall. Certainly he was unlike the local people who were wiry and slight. He spoke the local dialect well, but with an accent which showed the language was as foreign to him as it was to me. A dull green shirt stretched tightly across his barrel chest, the buttons straining to contain him. Heavily muscled arms, like those of a heavyweight wrestler, filled the short sleeves. His creased grey trousers were sweat stained round the waistband and grubby down the fly. They contrasted harshly with fluorescent pink socks and white plastic sandals. In the humid air, beads of perspiration coated his broad chocolate forehead. A thin scar ran from the corner of the right eye down the broad expanse of his nose to the corner of his mouth. His face and his overall appearance held a distinct aura of menace that was increased rather than dispelled by the brief smile as he finished eating.

He tossed the mango pip casually out of the open door and wiped his sticky fingers on the leg of his pants. Turning to look at me again, his eyes burned in the dim light. Again the tremor of apprehension fluttered through me and I hoped that it had not shown. I did not know this man. He was not someone I would forget easily and I wondered who he was and why he had come.

For a long moment we stared at each other as though neither knew what to say. Finally my visitor broke the silence. This time he spoke in good but heavily accented French. I tried to place his accent but could not.

"I am Kuloni Nkese. Do you know me, Kamran?"

His name was all too familiar and he evidently knew something about me for he had used the name by which the villagers now called me. It was the common name for a tall thin tree that grew in this part of the forest which Olidange, one of the villagers, had applied to me since I was over a foot taller than him and he had to crane his neck back to talk to me. The others, who were not much taller, all laughed and the name stuck. Word travels fast in the

forest, even among isolated communities, so I should not have
been surprised that Kuloni Nkese knew this. Even so, his use of the
name made the back of my neck tingle.

And with good reason. When people spoke his name it was with
fear and with hate, invariably accompanied by a sign to ward off evil
spirits. This man was the Party agent from a village some twenty-five
kilometres to the east of here, across the Banaii River. He was hated
by all, feared by most and spoken of well by none.

"I've heard of you," I replied neutrally. "I heard that you live at
Kimwamwa," I continued, as if compelled to speak by his very
presence.

"That is so. What more have you heard?" The glint was there in
his eyes again. He was enjoying this.

"Some speak of you with fear. Some speak with dislike because
they are wary of strangers and you are not of these people. Some
speak with respect," I replied evasively, not liking the way this
conversation was going.

"So!" The huge man laughed with a rumble that came from
deep in his belly and made him shake so that the old chair creaked
and squealed in protest at its burden. "And you, what do you say, my
friend?" His grin held all the menace of a hunting wolf, without its
lean ascetic dignity. "How do you judge me?"

Broadside: every question was a loaded one. I wanted him to
go, but now that I knew who he was I was also anxious to know why
he had come and what he wanted. Men like him do not visit
people like me in isolated forest villages for no purpose. After that
initial tingle of apprehension when he had used my local name,
alarm bells were now ringing inside me loud enough to raise
the ancestors.

I wanted him gone but I had to know why he had come. Kuloni

Nkese had an evil reputation and I had no wish to swell the ranks of those who had fallen foul of this particular Party Agent.

Legion were those who had reason to regret their encounters with Kuloni Nkese. I couldn't understand why the Party had never done anything about him. The Party was the *Mouvement Populaire de la Révolution,* or the MPR. It was the executive organ of the government in Zaïre. Divided into sectors, it exercised local authority, particularly in rural areas and, like any other political organisation in this continent, had huge defects. Whatever its failings, the Party did have rules and frowned on overt corruption. Abuse of authority such as this man was reputed to use could surely not be condoned.

Since coming to the country I had taken an interest in the local political system but always from the outside, as a detached observer. It was necessary to understand how things worked, if only to be able to cope with the ever-present mass of bureaucracy required for a foreigner to live and work here. But becoming politically involved was something I always tried to avoid. There were too many tales across the continent of outsiders who had meddled in local affairs, always with disastrous results. I had no wish to become one of them. Keeping an ear to the ground in order to know and understand what was going on is sensible enough and it can enable one to enjoy the country in harmony. Any involvement would be seen as meddling and lead inevitably to resentment and trouble.

Now this man seemed determined to involve me to a degree I always sought to avoid. True, I had met the President several times and carried, among my papers, his personal letter of authority for my work. But my acquaintance with Mobutu was a private matter and I hoped the man was unaware of our friendship. I had never advertised the fact, and that particular document was best saved for times when I might be confronted by unavoidable and otherwise insuperable bureaucracy.

This situation was something I had never foreseen. I would need to tread warily.

"What can I say? I've heard your name but I've never met you before, so I know nothing. I am not your judge, nor any other man's," I said. But of course I was, and I had already judged him.

"But you are," he boomed eagerly. "You have heard of me. You think of what you hear. Like any other man you will judge. So, how do you judge me, Kamran?" It was obvious that he would not let me off this hook. He would force me to commit myself in some way, which he would then pick to pieces and certainly turn to his own advantage.

Kuloni Nkese's French was formal and precise but his accent was unusual and harsh on the ear. It had a slightly guttural quality about it, unlike most francophone Africans who had gentle, rather musical accents. This was so different that I wondered where he could have learned it. Probably not from native francophones.

My thoughts raced as I wondered what had drawn this man into the Party and then driven him so that he built up the reputation that walked with his name in this region, and possibly elsewhere, for all I knew. This was not his sector and he should have no Party business here, least of all with me. If the Party had any business with me, it would have been the local man who sat here, and welcome, or else I would have been summoned to his office in town. Something told me that this was a personal matter and again I hoped that this man was not going to involve me in the sort of thing I had always managed to steer clear of.

His presence was oppressive and malignant He made my

home feel tainted. Little did I realise then that he was to do far more than that.

"I think you are a man who wants to ask for something, but I have no idea what it is," I said, trying to change the subject and make him declare himself.

He was not so easily diverted and was clearly enjoying my discomfort.

"You interest me, Kamran. First you lived in a smart house in the Portuguese district of the town, with electricity, taps full of water, and many rooms. Then, after only a short time, you leave and come to this place. What reason can you have to give up all that comfort and come to live in this… this mud hut?" Scorn fell heavily upon my ears as he spat the final words and gestured round my simple home with his arm.

I stared at him and said nothing. After a moment he continued.

"Why, I wonder, does an educated white man, a friend of the President, throw away such comfort and come to live among these stupid forest people? You are not one of the cursed missionaries who come to meddle with the spirits; to enslave men's souls and corrupt their children. You could live at ease, but you do not. But they tell me you choose… to live like this!" His tone was heavy with derision as he waved his arm again. "You are a mystery, Kamran, and this worries me. I don't like mysteries in my sector."

The last words were almost hissed. The gleam in his eyes showed a malevolence which clearly said he enjoyed bullying people. This time it was at my expense. Although I thought myself reasonably resilient to harsh words, he had caught me unawares and rattled me. I began to have sympathy with the unfortunate mouse quivering under the watchful gaze of a stalking cat, and wondered how many others had received this sort of attention from the big Party agent. When he mentioned the President, I groaned inwardly and hoped that perhaps Kuloni Nkese thought there was more to the relationship than was actually there. If he did it might just stop him going too far for fear of greater wrath. Some hope; for this man, I was to realise later, was a law unto himself.

"Have you taken over this sector, then?" I asked. "I was talking to Nkwanu Knaii yesterday and he said nothing about being replaced here. Has he been promoted to another post?"

The big man said nothing. Suddenly he rocked the protesting chair backwards onto its back legs and watched me intensely through half-closed eyes. I carried on, feeling very uncomfortable, trapped into answering his other questions.

"It was Nkwanu Knaii who told me about this house and who helped me to arrange things. He knows why I choose to live here and sees no mystery in it."

Abruptly the smile faded from Kuloni Nkese's face and he rocked forward to rest his elbows on his knees so that he loomed over me where I was seated on the floor.

When he spoke again it was softly and in complete contrast to his previous manner.

"That girl outside, pounding manioc, she is your woman?"

At first I was not sure whether it was a statement or a question. Now that he mentioned it, I became aware of the rhythmic thump of the heavy pestle crashing into the huge hollow *kumpunu* log to pound the dried tubers into flour. It was one of those sounds that is so much a part of village life one takes it for granted. I could not see her, but the image formed in my mind of the girl at her work. Smooth flowing and repetitive, her movements had a fluid grace that made them physical poetry to complement the tone poem I knew she would be humming to help maintain the rhythm.

The question startled me. Again I felt that twinge of apprehension.

"Abélé?" I answered obliquely. "She has no family and no house. She's only a child. It was arranged that she should live here and clean the house and cook the food. In this village, I am her guardian, her father."

"She lives here? She sleeps here, in this house?" The last word was loaded with scorn and at last gave me some direction for his questions.

"She sleeps on that mat," I said pointing to a rolled grass mat tied with raffia and propped against the wall. "Outside if it is dry, inside when it rains," I added unnecessarily as if justifying something that needed no explanation and was, in any case, none of his business.

"Do you use her?"

His question sounded enthusiastic and his manner was obscene. In a flash the prudishness of my Western upbringing raised its hackles. How dare he come into my house with his crude suggestions and probing insinuations?

The normal peaceful harmony of my home had been rudely shattered by his intrusion, but any fear I may have felt now turned to anger. "Abélé is only a child! She is as a daughter to me! She cleans the house and prepares food like any good daughter. That is all!"

Kuloni Nkese was delighted by my response. He threw back his great round head and let out a roar of laughter that made his fat belly shake. The cane chair protested and sagged a little more under his bulk.

"A woman as pretty as her lives in your house and you do not use her? Kamran, you are indeed a strange man. You are a mystery!"

As suddenly as it had begun his laughter stopped. He leaned forward again with his forearms on his knees. His voice was almost conspiratorial as he launched his next thrust.

"Tell me, my friend, how much do you want for her?"

I wished he would not call me his friend, but it was my turn for disbelief.

"What?" I spluttered. Surely he could not be serious. My ears must be deceiving me. This must be another of his efforts to disconcert me before he came to the point of his visit. If that was the case he had failed, for this just brought my anger fully to the surface.

"What do you mean? She's not a bloody donkey! Abélé is not some slave to be sold on a whim like a sack of yams. She's a child." He could see my anger and it evidently amused him. "What do you want with her, anyway?"

"I want her. What is her bride price?" he asked again, grinning broadly.

"She is not for sale. I've already told you!"

The grin stayed and laughter rumbled again in his belly. The cane chair creaked ominously. When he spoke again his manner was more formal and less taunting.

"I want her for my wife. It is the custom here to pay *ibene* to the girl's father, but since she has no father of her own, I must ask you. That is the custom." His face lost all expression as he continued. "I could just take her, but she is of little enough value and it amuses me to follow the custom, even though you are only her guardian, and a *mundele*."

This changed things considerably, for what he said about the bride price was quite true. A father or guardian was obliged to hear any serious petition and to set a price. Cunning devil, he had trapped me into a form of involvement that I had never even conceived.

It was all too sudden. The implications were too great for my sluggish brain to handle so fast.

I needed time.

"So, Kamran, what do you ask? What is her *dot?*" His question broke into my racing thoughts as I tried to find a way of legitimately denying him what he asked.

Outside Abélé had stopped her pounding and I could hear her scraping the flour into a basket. She would have prepared enough for two or three days and tomorrow she would sieve the flour and start the long process that would result in a heavy porridge, spiced with peppers and with a texture like old wallpaper paste. We ate a starch like this every day, with a variety of sauces and occasionally meat or fish. Mostly it was made from yams or other forest roots, but occasionally I bought manioc or grain when I went to Kikwit.

The afternoon light was fading now and it had become quite dark in the house. Even so I could still see the malicious glint in Kuloni Nkese's eyes. The silence brought with it a ray of hope and I realised how to get rid of the monster, at least for the time being. I would have time to think; time to talk with the villagers and ask their advice about what to do with this nightmare.

"You go too fast, Kuloni Nkese. You say that you're content to follow the custom. So be it. Tonight I will talk with Abélé and then consider this matter. I hear your request and, as custom requires, I will answer you, tomorrow," I said formally and he looked mildly surprised at my understanding of the local traditions. "You will go from here now, out of the village and back to your own house. Tomorrow you will come at the same time and, in front of witnesses, repeat your request if that is what you wish. Then I shall answer. Until this matter is settled you may not speak with Abélé. That is the custom. Now eat! Abélé is a good girl and makes fine food. She collects only the best fruit. If this thing is to be, you must learn to appreciate her true value."

I hated myself as I said this because the less he knew and understood the better, but I too was now committed to playing out this game according to the local rules.

I poured water into the glass, placed it near him, then picked up the basket of fruit and offered it to him. Kuloni Nkese looked blankly at me as though he could not understand why I had not instantly agreed to name a price. He was about to speak, but thought better of it.

He took another mango and sank his teeth into it as he glared at me. He was obviously angry at being tripped up, the more so since he had done it to himself. I hoped he was not already plotting revenge, but felt sure he would be.

"What do you know of the custom, white man?" He snarled through a mouthful of fruit.

"Enough for the moment," I replied, my anger subsiding rapidly now that I could see some respite, however temporary, from his onslaught. "You have chosen the way for yourself, Kuloni Nkese. Now you are committed to follow the custom. Have you the patience?"

"You know nothing. These are not your people," he muttered thickly and tossed the half-eaten fruit onto the floor as a thinly veiled insult. The atmosphere in the house felt as tense as a drum skin and I could feel my own heart thumping inside my chest.

It was dark in the house and even the bright aperture of the doorway was growing dim. Kuloni Nkese heaved his sweaty bulk out of the groaning chair and stood up. I rose too as he moved towards the door and leaned his arm against the lintel. He stared silently at Abélé clearing the ground where she had been working and I hoped he would not start some new trick. Perhaps there was still just enough of the traditionalist in him to make him keep his bond.

After several long moments he turned and straightened.

"You have made me welcome. I am honoured by your hospitality." He spoke once more in the local dialect, beginning the formal ritual of leave taking.

I heaved a mental sigh of relief. He had decided to keep the bond, for the moment.

"I am honoured by your visit. The house is honoured that you have eaten our food," I replied formally.

"Tomorrow I shall come."

With this he turned and ducked through the doorway. He strode off into the gathering dusk without once looking back. I went outside to watch him leave. His stride was an arrogant swagger, his bearing haughty. He looked round to make sure he was noticed. Soon he disappeared behind some bushes growing near the beginning of the track that would take him back to Kimwamwa. I wondered why he was on foot when he could have used his official vehicle.

I felt a surge of relief when he was finally out of sight and turned to look at Abélé. She was also watching the big man's departure, with an unmistakable look of fear on her face. As she became aware of me watching her, I smiled and she rushed over and flung her arms round me. She was shaking violently, a frightened child seeking comfort from her father.

I hugged her and, despite my own fears for what this affair

might lead to, I felt warm and rich inside. After a while she stopped shaking and loosened her hold just enough to look up at me. Her impish face made it easy to smile back. "It will be all right Abélé. Try not to worry. I won't let him hurt you." It was a promise that I had no idea how to keep, but I meant it.

"Will I make food now?" Abélé asked, loosening her grip a little more.

"Yes. You should prepare plenty. I'll ask Nkwanu Knaii and Ekwona and others to come. We need them to talk tonight so we should feed them well," I said.

Abélé brightened immediately at this. She always liked it when Nkwanu Knaii and the others came because they were kind to her and they liked her food.

"Will you go to the town for Nkwanu Knaii?" she asked. "You should bring some beer. And tin fish. What time will they come?"

"After the rain. Maybe nine o'clock," I told her. She nodded her understanding. Most of the villagers couldn't tell the time but Abélé had been keen to learn and I had hung a cheap clock on the wall by the door. She took great delight in winding it noisily every morning when she woke. Now I reached for my shirt that hung on a peg just inside the door and put it on.

Walking over to where my Land Rover stood under a large tree, I wondered how I was going to explain this awful mess to the villagers who had entrusted a young girl to my care. How would I explain it to Abélé herself? Would I be able to find a legitimate reason for denying Kuloni Nkese's request when he came tomorrow? If he came.

This could be some monstrous joke by him because he could find no other way of making trouble for me. Perhaps he would not come at all, leaving me, and Abélé, wondering when he would turn up, never knowing, never sure. But that would mean he had to give up the satisfaction of seeing my discomfort and I knew that he would be unable to stay away.

Stifling a futile curse, I kicked the Land Rover tyre in frustration.

Chapter 2

EVER SINCE I HAD OWNED IT, the Land Rover had been difficult to start. After months of living in the steamy forest, it was now a temperamental old heap with a mind of its own. It would cough and splutter any number of times before finally settling down to run smoothly. Weeks with little or no use didn't help. It had hardly been used at all during the last five or six weeks, since all my work had been within a few kilometres of the village and as roads in the forest were few and far between, it was generally easier to walk than to use the vehicle. In any case I enjoyed walking to and fro with the villagers; it helped break down any barriers there might have been between us. The camaraderie that developed enabled me to learn more about them and their customs and language and it provided further opportunities for them to get to know me. The friendship that had grown out of this might otherwise never have developed, for these people, although friendly, are very private when strangers are about.

There had been no large quantities of tools or materials to transport for some time, so the Land Rover had remained, untouched beneath its tree. Now, when I needed it to start immediately, the engine stubbornly refused to fire. It was almost as if I was being rebuked by the machine for my neglect.

The gloom of dusk was deepening rapidly so I turned the headlights on and took the plug spanner from the dash tray. The bonnet groaned as I levered it open to peer inside at the recalcitrant engine. By the reflected glow of the headlights, I removed and cleaned each of the spark plugs in turn, then dried out the inside of the distributor with a handkerchief. I could not help smiling as I did this, thinking of the countless times during childhood when my mother had told me off for using handkerchiefs for cleaning dribbling fountain pens or greasy bicycle gears instead of wiping my snotty nose.

With everything reassembled I went round and pressed the starter. The old engine roared lustily and settled to a steady grumble. That's my baby. You just needed a bit of regular petting, didn't you, I thought, wondering why one ascribes sentient attributes to troublesome machinery when attempting to master its foibles.

There was a slight buzz to the engine noise. The exhaust must have yet another hole in it. Like so many other components, it had been repaired several times with varying degrees of success. Eventually I would have to go to Kinshasa and buy whatever new parts were available; spares were hard to obtain in this outpost. Meanwhile it was mend and make do.

The old vehicle used to get far more attention until I persuaded the manager of the palm oil mill, a few kilometres downriver from the village, to give my young neighbour Mputu a job. Mputu loved machines and had a natural talent with anything mechanical; far more than I had myself. I had cause to be grateful to him and could have done with his nimble fingers to fix the lamp that still lay in pieces, strewn across the floor of my house. He loved to tinker and had kept the old engine spotless and running sweetly.

Mputu had wanted to go to the town and find work as a mechanic in one of the innumerable ateliers, but his father, Mpwanzu, had refused. He said his son was still too young to live alone in the town, and all his family lived here in the village. Why should he want to leave them?

Mpwanzu had talked it all through with me and I had discussed it with the manager at the mill. At first the manager had been doubtful and reluctant, but eventually he agreed to give Mputu a trial for a month. That had been five months ago. Now, each time we met, the manager told me exhaustively how pleased he was that I had persuaded him to take the lad on. Mputu spent long hours working on the machinery he loved and was being well paid and well trained into the bargain. There was pure delight and pride in his eyes whenever he talked about the mill and its machines.

Mpwanzu was satisfied too since his son was home every two or three days and his accommodation at the mill was much better than he could have found in some hovel on the fringes of the town, wondering where the next mouthful of food was coming from. Mputu also brought money to his family.

I thought of all these things as I drove through the village and stopped in front of Ekwona's house. Ekwona was an old man, a forest villager now in his fifties where the normal life expectancy was generally no more than thirty-five or forty. He was Mputu's uncle and, although he had no formal title, was greatly respected for his wisdom and accepted by everyone as the village headman. Ekwona was a small man who kept his whole head cleanly shaven. His heavily pitted face bore witness to the smallpox he had survived as a youth and made the brightness of his eyes that much more dramatic. Added to this, his face would crinkle with an infinite variety of expression as he talked.

Ekwona was sitting on a large rock outside his house as I pulled up. He was puffing at an acrid smelling cheroot and watching the fireflies perform their nightly aerial ballet.

"Kamran, I see you are getting too old to walk now!" He teased as I climbed from the cab and touched his outstretched fingers in greeting. "If your chariot is broken, it will have to wait until tomorrow. Mputu is working at the mill tonight."

His voice was light and his eyes glittered with fun; very different from the eyes I had so recently been watching with morbid apprehension. His manner was warm and companionable as he shuffled aside so that I could share his rock.

"I'm not looking for Mputu," I said. "I had a visitor today and it has disturbed me. I need wisdom from those who know things."

"The man from Kimwamwa." It was a statement; he had no need to ask. "When that man is near you should take care."

"Yes. I see word has spread already. He's only been gone a few minutes."

"I saw him. Éyéee! Éyéee! What have you done to anger the spirits so that they send you a devil such as him?" Ekwona asked with mock alarm, the smile in his eyes reflected in the glowing tip of his cheroot.

He offered me one of the evil smelling things. I accepted and lit it from the one he smoked. I didn't like these forest cheroots with their taste like burned compost, but they kept away the swarms of biting insects that populated the air around dusk each evening. For several minutes we sat and smoked in silence, watching the fireflies courting.

"He wanted Abélé for a wife," I said in explanation. "I've sent him away, but he will come again tomorrow. Then I must have an answer for him and I don't know what to do."

We smoked again in silence, watching the fireflies and listening to the gasping croak of the frogs down by the river. After a while Ekwona got to his feet and stretched

"I will tell the others," he said decisively. "Nkwanu Knaii should come also. Will you bring him?"

"Yes. That's why I brought the Land Rover. I'm going to the town to ask him now. Abélé is making food." I moved towards the Land Rover. "Will you bring a lamp, Ekwona? Mine is broken. I was trying to mend it when that man came. It's still in pieces on the floor."

"We have lamps. We will all come." He nodded and disappeared into the darkness.

THE ENGINE CAUGHT FIRST TIME and I manoeuvred round behind the houses and onto the forest road that led up to the town six kilometres away. The road, no more than a track really, was rough at the best of times. This was the wet season, which meant that it rained for six hours every day, instead of only four. In consequence, the twisting surface of the road was further carved by deep channels, where the run-off from the heavy rain had found new courses in its headlong dash down to the river that snaked through the valley bottom.

It was slow going, in low gear, with the Land Rover leaning crazily one way and then the other as the road twisted and turned over the heaving forest floor, skirting the trunks of huge inyaba, kapok, fig trees and others, some of which were probably still unnamed. Heavy undergrowth brushed along both sides of the vehicle and cut visibility down to no more than a few yards. I hoped I would not meet anything coming the other way.

The night air was rich with the mingled scents of exotic tropical blooms and the rank stench of rotting vegetation. Swarms of nocturnal insects were caught for brief moments in the glare of the headlights before vanishing into the stygian blackness. Some of them found their way inside the cab and buzzed furiously around my ears and nose. I puffed vigorously at Ekwona's cheroot, reducing the visibility still further by filling the cab with dense smoke.

In the village clearing, close to the river, there had been room for at least some air movement. But here, in the deep forest, it was more stagnant and humid than ever. By the time I reached the slope where the road climbed out of the forest towards the town, my shirt was soaking wet and clinging to my body. Higher, in the town, the air became cooler and as I pulled up beside the wall surrounding Nkwanu Knaii's house, I could feel the first stirring of the evening breeze.

A tall kapok tree stood in the walled compound, its sheer trunk studded with thick, stubby thorns. By day the tree gave shade to the house and some of the courtyard, but in the light of the rising moon it cast a sinister shadow. This was a tree of the deep forest, left behind when the jungle had been driven back by the town's expansion. It would have been more at home in the high gallery forest of the river valley where many of the trees topped two hundred feet, their flat canopies lacing together to form an intricate green tapestry of strange shaped leaves and exotic blossoms over the rank tangle of the jungle below.

The forest canopy was hidden by the fold of ground over which the road meandered. Behind me, the foreground was a patchwork of small fields and vegetable gardens where townsfolk had cleared the scrub to grow a little supplementary food. Above the nearby rooftops there was a scattering of other surviving kapok trees. They stood like sentinels in the moonlight, watching over the cascade of jumbled, shapeless buildings and a thousand twinkling lights.

Attracted by the noise of the Land Rover, four small children tumbled merrily out of the doorway. A naked bulb inside the house cast a bright shaft of light onto the swept earth of the compound. The children crowded round, chattering and bubbling with laughter. I hoisted the smallest onto my shoulders and the others redoubled their cries for attention. As I walked towards the house with the children milling round my legs and holding their outstretched hands, their mother appeared in the doorway to find out what all the noise was about.

"You have beautiful children Akanku," I said, lifting the baby down from his perch and giving him to her.

"I know it. And it is too long since they have seen their uncle from the forest. I have wondered what we did to make you hide from us," she chided gently, her face alight with a welcoming smile.

"Working, not hiding. But you are right, it has been too long, and you've still not come to see my house. You must bring the children to the village and I'll make a boat so that we can all play in the river," I said, returning her sisterly embrace.

"Come in and eat with us," Akanku said as she ushered the last of her brood back into the house.

"I'd like that, Akanku, but tonight I can't stay. There is trouble and the village men are waiting for me to return. I came to find Nkwanu and ask if he will come and talk with us. Abélé is making food for everyone."

"Eh! She is a good girl that one. Some day she will make someone a good wife."

"That is precisely the problem," I replied. "She is only a girl. But now a man, a bad man, has asked for her."

Akanku and her sons.

Akanku stopped what she had been doing, straightened up and looked directly at me. "Has she started her moons?" she asked.

"Yes. Two months ago."

"Has she talked to the village women about it?"

"I don't know. Probably not. You know her story. They're unlikely to seek involvement but I don't think they would brush her off if she asked. After all, they cared enough to arrange her fostering with me," I said. "I talked with her and did my best to explain. I think she understands and she makes no fuss over it. Perhaps I should have brought her to talk to you. She likes you, Akanku."

"Of course you should, you fool. You are a good man, Kamran;

gentle and kind and easy to talk to, but this is women's business. You cannot know the things that need to be said." Her spreading hands told me off as much as her words and tone. "I like Abélé too, and will come and talk with her. You understand that now this has happened she will be considered a woman and so she is ripe to be a wife?"

"Yes. But she is only thirteen. I can't give her to some man almost three times her age; one who will certainly abuse her and treat her like an animal. She should have a young man who shares the sunlight in her eyes, who will care for her and treat her well. She's had enough misery in her life already."

"Éyéee! We all dream, Kamran, especially for our children. I am lucky, Nkwanu is a good man. Few can hope for one like him. Who is this man that asks for Abélé?" She asked.

I hesitated to say the name. Akanku looked at me questioningly. "Who is he?"

"Kuloni Nkese," I said flatly.

"Éyéee!" She gasped. "That one! The ancestors must be angry to send that one." The alarm in her voice was reflected in her face. "Nkwanu is still at the Party office. He has a lot of work preparing for the big meeting next month, but he'll go with you."

"I'll come back when I can," I said, moving towards the Land Rover.

"Come soon, and bring Abélé with you," Akanku said. "We shall all come to visit you soon, and you can make the boat you keep talking about." She slammed the Land Rover door as I started the engine, and waved me off.

I drove towards the centre of town where the Party office was situated. The place was ablaze with lights, which spilled out of windows and doorway to illuminate the dusty street. In the bright rectangle made by the light from the front door lay one of the town's stray dogs, gleaning the last of the day's heat from the warm earth of the road. The dog twitched an ear but took no notice of me as I drove round him to park in front of the official Toyota outside the office. A face peered out of the window to see who was coming, then withdrew.

Nkwanu Knaii could be heard clearly as I approached the office. He was talking rapidly into the telephone. He looked up briefly and smiled, nodding to the bench under the window, then turned his attention back to the papers on his desk and the voice on the other end of the telephone. It was obviously a bad line; they always were. He was speaking loudly and frequently asking for something to be repeated. It sounded as if they were discussing one of the Party's regular public education meetings to be held in the forthcoming weeks. These had become a regular feature of life in Zaïre where every adult was automatically a member of the MPR and had to do their duty towards the President's national unity initiative by attending Party meetings. In some places, these took the form of hard line indoctrination. In this sector, things were a bit more subtle and the meetings were more like happy social gatherings with a little Party doctrine thrown in. As a result they were generally well attended with the audience amenable and compliant.

The assistant brought me tea, which I drank while reading the Party notices and posters pinned to the office wall and waiting for Nkwanu Knaii to finish his call. At last he cradled the handset with an exasperated sigh and pushed his fingers through his hair, leaning back in his chair and stretching.

"So, Kamran, what brings you to the town at night? Is there a problem, or have you come for a family visit?" he asked. "Akanku

Nkwanu Knaii with citizens at the door of the MPR sector office.
His light touch made him a popular administrator.

and the children will be pleased to see you. You haven't visited us for weeks."

"It's not a social visit, I'm afraid. I have a problem and need your advice. The village men are coming to my house tonight to talk. I came to ask if you would come too."

"Trouble in the village?"

"No, the villagers are all fine, but a man from outside came to see me today and I don't know how to answer him. I need advice."

"Who was this man, and what did he want?" he asked, leaning forward with interest.

"He is called Kuloni Nkese. He asked me to name the bride price for Abélé."

"Éyéee! That one is trouble, to be sure. I have a lot to do here, but it must wait. I will come. Go back to the village. I will be there in one hour."

"Abélé is making food," I said, nodding my thanks.

"I'll be there sooner," he laughed. "She makes good food."

The dog was still asleep in the middle of the road as I climbed into the Land Rover again. The engine was still warm, so it fired immediately. I drove round to one of the small shops I used regularly, bought beer and sardines as Abélé had asked, then headed back to the village, my mind full of turbulent thoughts and doubts.

Chapter 3

THE SKY HAD CLOUDED OVER in the brief time that I had been in town and the evening rain began before I left the high ground to descend again into the forest. Its onset was heralded by vivid flashes of lightning which illuminated the country in stark relief and charged the air with static. This lasted for only about five minutes before heavy drops began to splatter against the windscreen and beat their random tattoo on the battered roof of the cab. The sultry evening air cooled noticeably from one moment to the next as the rain increased. Within moments I was enveloped in a roaring cascade that felt almost solid, as it pounded the ground and shook my old Land Rover.

At this time of year, the rain began in this way every evening, soon after dark. I had hoped it would hold off long enough for me to get back to the village, but luck wasn't smiling on me tonight. The roar of the rain hitting the vehicle completely drowned the noise of the engine. The windscreen wipers were ineffectual. Visibility diminished instantly to nothing and I was forced to a slithering halt just below the big bend where the road turned downhill toward the forest fringe.

This initial onslaught would last for about half an hour and I knew there was no point in trying to continue until it eased off. I closed the windows, snapped shut the dashboard scuttles to reduce the amount of water that was already pouring into the leaky old cab, then sat back to wait. At least there was one benefit from the rain, I thought: it had washed away the clouds of biting insects.

I made no attempt to move off the road, for no other vehicles would be moving until the rain eased. Later, when the clouds had lost their overburden and the rain settled down to a steady fall, there might be something, but few vehicles moved at night in this part of the country and, given the terrible state of the roads, those that did venture out would not be moving fast. Of course Nkwanu Knaii would be coming along behind me later, but I would probably be back in the village well before then. He wouldn't set out until the first downpour had eased.

Thinking of Nkwanu Knaii and his reason for coming roused again the turmoil of my emotions. I sat through the next half-hour trapped physically by the rain and mentally by dread of Kuloni Nkese. With the ferocity of the downpour and the agonies in my mind, the moment lacked only the doom-laden cacophony of Wagner's music to make the torment of Hades complete.

Eventually the storm eased and the downpour reduced to the steady rain that would continue for another three hours. Long before midnight it would cease altogether, leaving the night air cool, clean and refreshed until dawn. In the predawn hours the clouds would roll back, exposing the clear, bright heavens, strewn with a silver glitter of stars until the sun rose to lose them in the pale canopy. By mid-morning, small fluffy clouds would be forming, randomly at first, then in long lines like gathering regiments. Occasionally these would grow fast into wet mountains that released short sharp showers over the jungle. Usually the cloud cover would grow steadily and thicken until by mid-afternoon the sky was obscured by a heavy grey blanket. This stifled the forest and seemed to compress the air until it was again a rank, oppressive well of humidity, heat and putrefaction, intensifying until the gravid clouds once more erupted and shed their burden after dusk.

In the soggy air, the engine laboured slightly and I was glad I had kept it running through the worst of the storm. Being so temperamental, it would certainly have refused to start now. As the rain eased further, I engaged the four-wheel drive in low gear, moving off slowly on the slippery inclined surface.

The road deteriorated as it entered the forest. In places I was driving along in a raging, axle-deep torrent. Water streaming off the trees and rushing down from the high ground was carving new channels and hiding the holes and roots that could tear the front wheels off a vehicle trying to travel at anything faster than a crawl. As it was, the old Land Rover was continually pitched up and down and rolled from side to side, sometimes so sharply I thought it must surely overturn.

Eventually I came to the huge tree with three deep gashes cut in its buttress root. This marked the turning at the beginning of the steep track down to the village. More soil had been washed away here and the vehicle slewed round sharply as I made the turn, crunching its rear against the tree. Another dent in its battered body, I thought. It would have to be beaten out later. Slipping, sliding and bumping over the uneven surface, I followed the narrow track down towards the village and was relieved when at last the slope began to level out.

It was still raining when I drove through the village and parked under the big tree near my home. A number of men, some carrying hurricane lanterns, were heading towards the house. Most wore long, broad hoods of woven palm leaves to protect them from the rain. Looking like stiff capuchin capes, these reached down to their knees. They were like huge sacks that had been opened along one side and gave people the appearance of surrealist giant moths performing some awkward waddling gavotte as they were caught in the beam of my headlights, weaving their way between the puddles.

Ten or more people had already arrived, as witness the rain hoods stacked against the wall under the broad overhanging eaves. Others soon followed. The small house became crowded with people seated all round the room, on the floor, on stools and on my bed or standing against the wall, wherever space permitted. Several lanterns had been hung from the rafters and another stood on the small table beside the pieces of my own lamp, which someone had thoughtfully lifted from the floor. The cane chair was unoccupied and the grass mat on which I usually sat remained clear.

I looked at the faces, recognising them all, and noted that almost every married man in the village was present. None of the women would have come, but I half expected Abélé might be there. I wondered where she was, but felt no anxiety at her absence. One of the men, seeing my glance, told me the headman's wife had come and taken her. The married women were all assembled at Ekwona's house. Abélé would be brought back later, but would remain outside until I called her.

As late arrivals squeezed in and people moved round to make space for them, we heard the sound of another vehicle arriving. A few moments later Ekwona entered, carrying his own stool, followed by Nkwanu Knaii, who seated himself in the cane chair, acknowledging greetings from all around the room.

Ekwona looked around the assembled company, mentally checking that everyone was there before raising his hand for attention. The burble of conversation subsided to an expectant hush and everyone looked at the headman.

"When Kamran first came here he was a stranger, but he has eaten the *ebuga* root and we have seen his spirit. Now he is our brother." He paused as those present signalled their agreement. "Because we asked it, he became the father of the child none of us could accept in our families but who is, even so, our own child." This produced grunts of dissent from a few and nods of confirmation from most of the others. "We all know of the man who came to the village today. He has demanded that Kamran set *ibene* for his daughter."

Word spreads fast in a small community, so it must already have been common knowledge, but this public declaration of the problem facing the community produced a startled response and cries of denial, accompanied by much hissing, head shaking and sucking of teeth. No face in the house showed anything but revulsion for the proposal. A number of people had been strongly against my fostering the girl since, given her origins and heritage, they were uncomfortable with her presence in the village. But equally, no-one would actively do anything to harm her. Now that she had a proper home she was once more a legitimate member of the community whose status derived from my own.

After a few moments Ekwona resumed. "Kamran has learned our language and our ways. He lives by them as we do. He knows he must answer the demand. He has asked our counsel before he makes his reply."

"What can we tell him?" someone asked, "The decision must be his alone. We cannot tell him what to ask."

"He should refuse," said another.

"Tell him she is not yet ripe," someone else suggested.

This unhelpful discussion was batted back and forth for several minutes as people gave vent to their feelings about the impossible dilemma. Few remained silent. Eventually, Nkwanu Knaii indicated that he had something to say and the gathering calmed to a respectful silence.

"You are all saying that we cannot tell Kamran what to ask, but this does not help. Would any of you wish his own daughter to become the wife of Kuloni Nkese?" he asked, and was answered by a sucking of teeth and shaking heads. "No, you would not. So use your knowledge to help now. It is true we cannot tell Kamran what he should ask, but in our tradition there are many things that can be asked by a father and some things that cannot be asked. We can tell him of these things. We have all paid the bride price for our own wives. We can tell him this. Some of you have daughters who are now married. We can tell him what was asked for them and how their price was decided. We can tell him the things about a bride that are desirable and how they relate to worth. We can tell him the things that are undesirable and how these reduce a bride's worth. All these things we can tell him, so that he will be wiser when he decides." He paused and looked around the assembled company, some of whom looked slightly ashamed.

"We can tell him what we know of Kuloni Nkese, even if there is nothing good to say, so that he may truly understand his character. We can tell him how a father considers the nature of the man who would take his daughter. We can tell him those things which helped us form our own decisions on such a matter. With all these things Kamran can use the wisdom of the whole village to help him decide. Abélé is a child of this village and deserves this much."

In the silence that followed this speech there were nods of agreement but nobody seemed willing to speak first.

"Tell me first what you know of Kuloni Nkese," I suggested to nobody in particular, and several began at once to tell me. "I want to hear you all," I called out over the noise, "but not at the same time, for then I can hear no-one."

The voices subsided and a man opposite me flicked his hand for my attention. I nodded for him to speak. In turn, they told me what they knew, much of it hearsay and opinion, but also many solid facts. A few, to their obvious discomfort, had even had direct dealings with Kuloni Nkese and these were recounted in exhaustive detail. It all formed a picture that gave substance to the impressions I had formed during my own encounter that afternoon.

Nkwanu Knaii, because of his position in the Party, knew more than anyone else and was able to put things in a more objective context. Even so, it was evident from the way he spoke that he, like all the others, despised the man and saw him as a major liability to the MPR and the people alike.

THE TALK WENT ON FOR SEVERAL hours during which I learned as much about these villagers as I learned about the Party agent from Kimwamwa. If I didn't already know these people well, I certainly knew them better after this.

They told me that Kuloni Nkese came originally from one of the eastern provinces. He was the son of a mission-educated farmer who had married a WaTutsi woman from Rwanda. In turn Kuloni Nkese had been educated by the mission and, although no genius, had gained a place at a secondary school in the provincial capital, Lubumbashi. During his time there he was frequently in trouble, usually for bullying people smaller or weaker than himself. On one occasion he had been arrested and charged with raping one of the junior girls at the school. He beat up two of the witnesses, intimidated others, and the charge was dropped for lack of evidence. Some days later the girl was found dead in a field some distance away, but nothing could be proved about how she died.

After three years at the school, Kuloni Nkese left and returned to his family, but he could not settle and moved away to a town where there were several factories and timber mills. He soon became involved with workers' committees and whenever there was any form of disturbance he was right there in the thick of things, rabble rousing, bullying and throwing his weight about. By this time he had grown tall and heavy, an unmistakable figure in any gathering.

Because of the fear he engendered, Kuloni Nkese soon gained influence and came to the attention of a local Party official. This man recruited him with promises of greater power and he was sent away for political training. Once he was in the system, the Party leaders soon saw tremendous potential in this great bull of a man. In the late Sixties, he was sent abroad to Patrice Lumumba University in the Soviet Union for further indoctrination and political training. He was as untamed there as he had been at home and must have been an uncomfortable guest for the Soviets. They were patient, however, and somehow managed to instil a solid foundation of their political theories as well as making him fluent in French and Russian.

The Russians did little to restrict his domineering manner, but taught him to employ it more effectively. There were a number of complaints from other students at the university who had fallen victim to his bullying and exploitation. The only restriction placed on him, however, came after the committee of a local farming commune complained that he had taken his pleasure one afternoon with no fewer than five of their young girls, in a field of turnips. The political commissar at the university sent for him and told him that if he ever touched another Soviet woman he would be castrated and made to eat his own testicles. He obviously believed the commissar for, from then on, he confined his activities to the other African students at the university.

Eventually the Soviets had done all they could with him. Kuloni Nkese was sent home and seconded to a Party branch office in Kinshasa. He soon gained a reputation as a hectoring bully and was employed on a number of occasions as bodyguard to senior Party officials when they made trips to the provinces. He liked the status this gave him and clearly enjoyed pushing people around, but it wasn't enough. He wanted to be the boss himself, but didn't possess the organisational skills and self-discipline to earn such a post on merit. Not to be put off, he set about an alternative campaign to improve his position.

Some days after returning from a trip to the provinces, Kuloni Nkese went on leave. The day after he left, the two officials whom he had accompanied on tour provided dinner for the crocodiles in the Congo River.

Allegations were made when Kuloni Nkese returned the following week, but he produced a hotel keeper from a town more than a hundred miles away who said that he had been in his hotel all the time, with a young girl and her mother. These two swore he had been in bed with them both at the same hotel from before the time the two men vanished until several days after their remains were discovered.

Two nights later, another senior official disappeared and was never found. When questioned, Kuloni Nkese produced a whole football team and several other people who claimed that he had been with them, drinking in a well-known bar all night long.

Kuloni Nkese had made no secret of his desire to be top man, but the Party was becoming increasingly uncomfortable with him. The situation would be even worse with him as a senior official and some wanted to get rid of him, but others felt he could still be useful. In the end they compromised and he was sent to be the Party's sector agent at Kimwamwa.

This was a small sector, with only two officials, two hundred miles away in the deep forest. Four days after Kuloni Nkese's arrival, the other agent fled into the forest and was not seen for nine weeks. Kuloni Nkese did not bother to report the matter and was effectively left in sole charge of the sector.

The other man did turn up eventually. He walked into Nkwanu Knaii's office one day, exhausted and half starved, covered in scars and burn marks as if he had been branded. He claimed that the big brute had tortured him with a knife and by continually prodding him with a heated iron rod. One night he had managed to escape into the forest where he had been hiding ever since. Nkwanu Knaii had taken photographs of the man's injuries, but since they had been received in another sector and he had only the victim's word for how they were inflicted, he was not able to do anything about it.

Since then Kuloni Nkese had earned himself a steadily deteriorating reputation for cruelty, extortion, intimidation and extreme violence, through an incessant string of nefarious activities. It was hardly surprising, I thought, that I had felt so uncomfortable with his presence the previous afternoon.

THE TALKING HAD NOW BEEN going on for several hours and people were becoming a little restive. I stood up and worked my way towards the door. As I reached it, Abélé appeared out of the darkness and took hold of my hand.

"It's all right, Abélé," I reassured her. "You have nothing to be afraid of with these friends. Have you made food?"

"Yes. Also I took the beer and tin fish from the car."

"Good. Bring them now and we will eat."

She let go of my hand and I went back inside. Moments later she followed, handing out leaf-wrapped packages from a basket. Each contained a portion of *foufou* and a few sardines with a peppery sauce folded into the middle. Normally food would be offered in the cooking pot or a wooden bowl, but this was customary for a serious meeting, such as was being held this evening. Ekwona's wife had instructed her when I was away in the town and the final preparation had been done under the eaves, just outside the door, while we talked. Abélé, I knew, had heard everything. This was intended, for a girl needs to know how she is valued and what sort of a man she may be given to.

When Abélé brought in a large basket of fruits and placed it on the table I was surprised to notice that my Tilley lamp, which had been in bits earlier in the evening, was once more assembled. I looked round the faces and stopped at Mpwanzu.

"Mputu taught me," he said, with a shrug of the shoulders. "That is a small return for what you have done for him." He lowered his eyes. He must have done it while we had been talking for I was sure it had still been in pieces when the meeting began.

"You have a good son, my friend. You will always have reason to feel proud of him. Thank you for mending my lamp."

As I sat down someone passed me a gourd of palm wine.

I looked at Abélé as I drank, and winked. She understood and disappeared outside, returning immediately with two crates of factory-made beer. The boxes were soon emptied and more were handed in from outside until everyone had a large bottle with the top off. Then the talking started again and I asked what things could not be asked in a bride price.

Liberally lubricated with more food, beer and palm wine, the talk flowed on through the night. At some point Abélé had abandoned her lonely vigil outside the door and crept in to sit beside me on my mat. She curled up small and leaned against me. Automatically I put my arm round and held her. She remained like that, eyes wide, patiently listening and trying to make sense of the words that could have such an important influence on her future.

It must all have been very confusing to Abélé. I found it difficult enough to understand the complexities of what could and could not be asked in the bride price, tangled as things were by the intricacies of taboos, relative status of the various parties, and the convoluted relationships and obligations of the African extended family system.

While I could, and did, ask questions, these also were limited by complex traditions and local customs. I knew that in the end I would have to make my decision alone. There are conditions under which a father could refuse to name the bride price, but they clearly did not apply in this case. I would have to commit myself.

It was not permitted for me to ask directly whether what I wanted to claim was admissible for, besides Abélé's future, my wisdom and value as a father were on trial. This would be judged by what I decided and the *ibene* I set.

This dilemma had sharp horns indeed, and they were barbed, with no easy escape. There was no option but to see this through to its conclusion and try to engineer the situation to the best I could. Kuloni Nkese, of course, had known all this and was probably at this moment gloating over the agonies I was forced to endure.

Complicated as things were, my friends were very patient with me and slowly, as dawn approached, I became aware of a sense of order in the mass of information they had shared with me.

Those who had daughters told me how they valued them and what bride price they had asked. Others extolled the virtues of their own wives and recounted what they had been asked to pay for them. They explained how the attributes of young women were identified and the worth these gave them as they led me gently along the tortuous pathway of decision.

AS DAWN APPROACHED, THE village women came and stoked up Abélé's cooking fire outside. She got stiffly to her feet and went out to join them and the gathering as one stretched and yawned, trying to shake off fatigue.

When Abélé returned she brought more leaf-wrapped parcels of food and respectfully handed one to each of our guests. She went out again and brought coffee, strong and sweet. A whole stalk of fat pink skinned bananas was produced and these too were received with enthusiasm and passed round.

She was about to go out again when I called her back.

"Abélé, stay here, I have listened to our friends all night and now I must ask you something."

Apprehension clouded her face as she sat down facing me. "Have I done wrong, Papa?" she asked, with eyes starting to fill with tears.

"No, no. You have done nothing to displease me," I reassured her. "I wish to know what you think of all this, and what you want, that is all."

She looked slightly less worried, but uncertain about what I was asking.

"You are a young woman now, and do much of a woman's work. Now, if your father agrees, you can become a wife and take on all the responsibilities of a woman. Do you understand?" I asked gently.

"Yes, Papa," she said in a small, tight throated voice.

"You saw the man who came to see me yesterday, and know that he has asked me to set the bride price for you. You know that I must answer him. Now, I must know what you want before I decide."

The expression of horror that spread across her face told me the answer before her startled cry. "No! Not that one. Another, if you wish it, but…" Her eyes flooded and with a choked sob she buried her face in my chest and flung her arms tightly round me.

I wrapped my own arms around her and rocked her gently until the flood of emotion died down, in each of us. The village men looked on in silence. All shared her dread of the man and all were obviously relieved it was I facing his demand, not them.

"Hush now," I said to Abélé, easing her hold slightly so that I could see her face. "I will never let him have you, never. I know it is frightening, but I had to know your wish. Now I know and it is the same as mine. I promise he will never touch you, Abélé."

The panic sobbing had subsided now. Slowly she sat back on her heels and looked at me with wide eyes. My smile helped her regain control and she wiped her face with the back of a hand and nodded.

"You know I cannot refuse his request to set the bride price, but I can set a price he will not pay. That is what I shall do," I explained. "He knows that without my permission he may not speak to you or come near you. He has committed himself to following the tradition in this matter, so for now you are safe. Even so, I will find a way of making you safer, so that you never have to be afraid again."

She had regained her composure. For one so young, it was remarkable and I admired her for it. I wished I could feel as calm as she appeared to be.

"Go with the other women now, and collect some fruit. When you come back, I want you to go with Nkwanu Knaii to the town." I looked at him and saw him nod his agreement. "He will take you to Akanku. You will stay with her and help look after her children until I come for you or Nkwanu Knaii brings you here again. Do you understand?"

"Yes, Papa," she replied, much more her bright self now. I knew she liked Akanku's children and the prospect of spending a few days with them was obviously attractive. She went happily out to join the other women.

"Éyéee! That is courage," Olidange said softly.

"Yes, she is very brave," I said.

"Not her, you."

"Why me?"

"To challenge Kuloni Nkese. That is the action of a fool or a brave man, and we all know you are not a fool."

"Thanks, but you can see I have no choice. None of you would willingly give your daughters to that man. Nor can I. Abélé has had enough misery in her life. She shall not have more."

"Some of us would kill our daughters rather than let him have them," someone else said.

"Then you would waste good daughters," I replied. "I would sooner kill Kuloni Nkese, for that would waste nothing."

"That is brave indeed. Many would bless you and praise your name," Ekwona said. "When he comes again you will have witnesses here to hear the bride price. Now, have we talked enough? I am sleepy."

"We have talked enough. I must think about all that has been said, and draw wisdom from your words. Thank you for your counsel, my friends. I will try to use it as wisely as it was given."

"We have eaten your food. We pay for it with words," Ekwona intoned.

"You have eaten Abélé's food," I told him.

"Then her worth is high, for the food was well made," he replied and stood up to take his leave. He shook Nkwanu Knaii by the hand, placed his palm on my forehead as if to hand me wisdom, and went.

In turn all the others did the same until there were only Nkwanu Knaii and myself left in the house.

Chapter 4

"I NEED TO WASH," I SAID, peeling off my shirt. "Will you come with me and swim in the river while we wait for the women to return?"

Nkwanu Knaii jumped to his feet with a big grin and followed me out of the house. On the riverbank I shed my clothes and dived into the gently flowing brown water. As I surfaced Nkwanu Knaii called me from the bank.

"Are you sure there are no crocodiles here?" he asked.

"There are hippos living on the small island just round the bend. Crocodiles won't stay in this part of the river while they are about," I reassured him, treading water ten yards from the bank. "None of the villagers or the fishermen from upriver has seen one for over six months."

He shed his own clothes and joined me in the water and we swam together across to the far bank and back. There was a huge tree growing on the near bank and its lower branches stretched out over the water in long sweeping curves. Some of the roots had been exposed when the river was in spate and they now formed a thick tangled web below the trunk and reached down to a small stony beach. Soon after coming to the village I had wedged a small basket among the roots where I kept a piece of soap. I clambered out of the water, collected the soap, then sat on the shingle and soaped myself all over. Nkwanu Knaii joined me on the beach and I passed him the soap.

Well-lathered, we went back into the water to rinse ourselves off and swim again. As we paddled lazily back and forth, dodging clumps of water hyacinth that drifted down on the current, we talked about the night's events. My friend explained again the limits of his own authority and those conditions that might possibly entitle him, as the regional sector head, to become involved, but neither of us could see that happening. My adversary – for that is what Kuloni Nkese had become – was far too wily to leave himself open to any such intervention.

Nkwanu Knaii was also a strong traditionalist and would offer no comment or suggestion that might pre-empt or influence my decision. While he was evidently very sympathetic to my position, the problem was mine alone to resolve. He had given me what knowledge and understanding he could, but the decisions would have to be mine. I thought back over all he had said, not just during the previous night, but ever since I had first met him.

OUR FRIENDSHIP HAD BEGUN just over a year ago, soon after I arrived in the country and had come to Kikwit town to find a house and set myself up. On arrival I had reported to the local MPR office, as all foreigners were obliged to do, to register my presence in their jurisdiction and seek advice. Half expecting the officiousness I had encountered in the capital, I was surprised to be received with courtesy and cooperation. I warmed immediately to the man in charge and we soon became friends.

From the outset Nkwanu Knaii was interested in the work I had come to do among the forest people and he proved to be very informative and helpful, introducing me to all the influential people in the local administration and telling me a lot about each of them.

He was a few years older than me and, although he originally came from this region, had travelled abroad and been well-educated. His father had worked for the national bank during the colonial era and had served for some years at their head office in Brussels. The family had accompanied him and Nkwanu Knaii and his two brothers received five years of first class education at a boarding school in Ghent. When the family came home, he had entered the university and studied for a degree in politics. His organisational skills had been noticed early on and the Party recruited and trained him.

For three years he had served in a number of minor posts, gaining experience and proving himself, before being sent to take over this neglected regional office. Since his arrival, five years ago, he had brought new life to the MPR. The Party was the main political driving force of the country, but instead of using it as a mechanism for control and domination, Nkwanu Knaii had used his position to bring real benefits to the people and had earned their respect, trust and support.

Soon after his return to the region he had married Akanku, a local girl whom he had known from infancy. She gave him three beautiful children who were his pride and joy. While Akanku had little formal education herself, she proved to be a wise and supportive wife with an instinctive understanding of her husband's aspirations and a level-headed pride in his achievements.

During our first meeting, Nkwanu Knaii had asked many questions about my work on rural water supplies and had made a number of useful suggestions. He had personally taken me on a tour of the surrounding villages, combining this with his own Party business, and ensured that I met all the village headmen whose support was vital if my programme was to achieve anything.

He taught me a great deal about the local culture and its customs and demonstrated how he exploited his own understanding of the people to involve them in the Party's activities. His style was gentle, persuasive and supportive. Wherever he went, he was received with goodwill and friendship. Under his husbandry, the Party had grown into a vigorous, well-supported organisation which held the respect and commitment of the population. He was a very effective promoter of Mobutu's campaign to create an authentic Zaïrois national identity.

IT HAD DONE ME NO HARM to be known as a friend of Nkwanu Knaii. Besides introducing me and educating me about the people and their ways, he and his wife had done a lot to help me to learn the local language, rapidly and fluently. He had also found me a good local teacher from whom I leaned the grammar. This was Batholomée, who worked for the Catholic mission and had somehow managed to retain his Christian name, despite the change required by Mobutu's so-called *authenticité* decree.

While Lingala was being introduced as the official national language, because it was Mobutu's own tongue, the basic language of the region was Kituba. Down in the forest, however, I was close to a tribal boundary and the people spoke a mixed dialect that included a lot of Tchipende words and phrases. Batholomée taught me the structure and Akanku and her husband gave me the dialect. The villagers of Inkwiti soon added their own peculiarities to my speech with the result that I spoke the way the locals did, not – like

Nkwanu Knaii and an MPR work cadre. This gang, which included four pygmies, were constructing a forest road.

most foreigners – in the distinctive style of the colonial missionaries who, although they had been the first to document and recorded the language, had somehow given it a character that only they used. By my speech it was clear that I lived in the forest and was neither a colonial nor a missionary.

Nkwanu Knaii introduced me to a number of local business people, some of them from old Portuguese families who, along with a few Belgians, had stayed on after independence. It was from one of these that I rented my first house in Kikwit. This was a colonial style bungalow on the western side of the town, beyond the commercial district and out toward the airfield. While it was a comfortable house and the neighbours were friendly, I felt isolated. It was also inconvenient since I had to cross the town, in itself a time-consuming process, and then drive down to the forest with its barely passable tracks, simply to get to where I was supposed to be working. Several hours travelling each day severely eroded my useful working time.

After three weeks I had discussed the matter with Nkwanu Knaii. He understood the problem immediately and agreed that it would make more sense for me to live somewhere in the forest, in one of the communities with whom I was trying to work. He had also found out enough about me to realise that having grown up in the African bush, I would have no problem adapting to the ways of the forest folk. Two days later he took me to Inkwiti and introduced me to Ekwona and some of the other villagers.

This village was one I had not yet visited but here, as in so many others, there was a significant problem with their water supply, even though the village was situated close to the bank of a large river. The river was used for washing and fishing but, because the water was usually heavily laden with silt, it was unpalatable for drinking or cooking. The fine sediment took days to settle out by gravity alone and the villagers had never developed the means of filtering it. As a result, the village women had to walk nearly a mile each way through the heavy forest to bring clean water from a spring, a few gallons at a time.

A mile may not seem like much, but in a dense tropical forest where the rampant growth starts to obscure a cleared path almost as soon as it has been cleared, this was hard going and very time-consuming. The village men had to attack the vegetation with machetes every few days just to keep the passage open and the spring accessible.

When Nkwanu Knaii explained about my work, Ekwona was immediately interested and insisted on making an immediate visit to Gijeni, one of the villages where work had already started. Would I go with him to explain it? I could hardly refuse, for such genuine interest was a heaven-sent opportunity.

Ekwona explained that we couldn't use a vehicle as there was no suitable road in the direction we needed to go. We would have to walk. It was obvious that this expedition was going to take more than the rest of the day so Nkwanu Knaii said he would leave me with Ekwona and come back for me the next afternoon. He climbed into his official Toyota and rumbled back to the town.

WHAT I HAD BLITHELY ENVISAGED as a gentle stroll through the forest turned out to be a far more serious expedition. Ekwona gathered five other men from the village, all armed with machetes, and we set off along a well-worn track. Within half a mile, this diminished to a narrow path and we were soon chopping and slashing at the undergrowth in order to make any progress.

The villagers neither tired nor hesitated as they hacked through the tangled vegetation. They told me cheerfully that this was an established path that just needed a little tidying up, although to me it seemed as though we were gnawing our way through virgin jungle. Taking turns to lead, they maintained a constant merry chatter that developed into a steady rhythm as they wielded their machetes with precise skill to clear our passage.

After an hour we came to a river. This was only a small stream, they explained, and with a lot of noise and a great deal of splashing we waded across. The men were in high spirits and it seemed as if they were making a game out of the whole venture. When I mentioned this to Ekwona, he told me that it was indeed different from their normal activities and so everyone was enjoying themselves. At the same time, there was a serious purpose to their behaviour as the noise warned any animals or people of our presence and reduced the risk of unexpected encounters. Some of the forest dwellers, people as well as wild animals, were inclined to attack when surprised. It also announced to the forest spirits that our purpose was without deceit and therefore we should be allowed to pass unmolested.

"But how can you hunt if you make so much noise?" I asked. "Surely it will frighten all the game away."

"When we hunt we are silent," Ekwona explained. "Before the hunt we prepare with ceremonies, to tell the spirits our intentions and to ask their permission."

"How do you know if they have agreed?"

"They allow us to catch meat." His tone was mildly mocking of my stupidity at failing to understand this most elementary fact.

"I can see I have a lot to learn," I said.

"If this thing Nkwanu Knaii has told me is true," Ekwona said, "you will teach us about the water. In return we will teach you about the forest. It is good, the forest."

His enthusiasm was evident, but this was early days and I was still struggling with the language. It took a few minutes for his offer to sink in. When it did, I felt a warm glow of satisfaction and goodwill towards this wizened man and his chattering friends.

We crossed three more streams in this manner during the next few hours. Occasionally our course crossed game trails and at one point we came to a large clearing where the remains of an abandoned village stood, open to the sky but heavily overgrown with vines, creepers and small bushes. Here the forest was vigorously regenerating itself.

With approaching darkness the men began to gather fruit whenever we came across a laden tree. One of them found some large snails. These were not just large, they were huge, weighing over two kilos each, and a single snail completely filled my cupped hands. I had never seen snails so big and might never have believed it if I had simply been told about them. They had thick shells of a rich chestnut colour with a thin golden line spiralling out from the central whorl. I was keen to keep one intact, but as soon as they were discovered the men smashed the shells, dug out the snails and skewered them on a sharpened stick. Later when they had been cooked I found that they were extremely chewy and tasted like musty muddy rubber. They were probably better smoked.

We had been walking for almost six hours by the time I began to think seriously about food and to wonder what time we might stop, when the jungle abruptly thinned and we came to a broad pathway. Not far along this was another rocky, bubbling brown stream with a few houses on the far bank. At last I saw something familiar and recognised where we were. This was Gijeni. The main part of the village was set back from the stream on a rise, with a narrow road beyond. I had been working here two weeks ago.

The villagers were not expecting to see me for another week and were surprised when I strolled in from the forest. They were even more surprised to see the men who accompanied me and a crowd soon gathered to greet the visitors and exchange news. After some minutes the headman appeared and held a noisy formal exchange with Ekwona. Once the formalities had been observed, we were led to a large structure at the far end of the village. This was no more than a thatched roof supported on thick posts that served as a meeting place for public talking and as accommodation for visitors.

Our men offered the fruit and snails, which were swiftly taken away by the resident women folk to be cleaned and cooked, while everyone else sat down to talk.

Ekwona explained the purpose of our visit and asked if the people would permit him to see the work on their spring. They readily agreed to this but, as it was now dark, said it would have to wait until morning. The exchange of news and food were far more immediate concerns.

Eating and talking went on late into the night and as the hours passed I realised that I was slowly becoming more proficient with the language, for I understood much of what was said and had to ask less frequently for words to be explained. The others could talk through the night, but I was tired after our long trek and kept nodding off. Eventually I moved to a quiet corner and lay down on a thick, springy mat of woven palm leaves. Sleep came quickly. The next thing I remember was being woken by people moving about and talking loudly. It was already light and food was being offered by our hosts.

TO MAKE ACCESS TO THE SPRING easier, particularly for the transport of building materials, the villagers had cleared a broad path uphill from the village. This was actually wider than the nearest road that passed along the top of the ridge, and was becoming easier to use as the daily passage of many feet and spilled materials had produced a compacted surface. With great pride they showed how they had cleared the area round the spring and collected rocks and gravel. The men would start burning charcoal for the filter next week, they told me, and showed where they had dug out the bank and prepared a closely packed layer of stones as a foundation for the spring's main filtration box, the walls of which had now been built.

The concept was simple enough and needed little explanation from me. The villagers were keen to show off and explain everything to their visitors, taking great delight in demonstrating the small model that I had built to show them what the work involved and what the finished filter would be like. We had dug back into the slope to expose the spring and create a level platform below it. Then a long walled box made of stones and cement had been built with four transverse chambers so that water collecting in the first would overflow into the second and then pass through narrow ducts in the bottom of the next wall. It would rise through the third chamber and spill over into the final one before flowing out through a valve into the villagers' containers. The first chamber was filled with gravel and the next with washed sand, brought from the nearby river. The third chamber was packed with lumps of hard charcoal, made nearby in the forest, with a few slabs of flat stone on top to hold it in place. The final chamber was simply a collecting tank. The whole assembly, which was about eight feet by four, was covered with a sloping thatched roof that had been plastered and sealed with cement. The framework for this had just been built when we visited.

Ekwona understood immediately he saw all this and was impatient to go back to his own village and get work started on their springs. He asked if I would make another model for his people and nodded happily when I said I would. He held an animated discussion with his friends while I spent a few minutes talking with the workers and leaving them instructions for the work that should be done next. By mid-morning we set off on the long trek back to Inkwiti.

Going back was much easier than the outward journey and even to my untutored eyes, the way was easily discernible. Even so there were numerous places where the vegetation had already reclaimed the narrow corridor our previous passage had carved. Long tendrils of creepers leaned across our way and some of the bushes beside the path seemed to incline inwards, as if trying to reach out to touch and console their neighbours whose branches had been slashed and broken by our machetes. We were back in Inkwiti by mid-afternoon and Ekwona was asking what materials were required for me to make their model. I said that I would bring all the necessary materials with me in a few days and asked to see the spring the village used. He told me there were three and, accompanied by a chattering entourage of inquisitive villagers, immediately led me off on a tour of them.

Word spread quickly as the other men told their families and friends about our visit to Gijeni. We soon had half the village following with small children scampering about between our legs and jumping out from behind huge trees with squeals of delight as we responded with mock fright. Rather like the BaMbuti people of the Ituri forest, far to the north-east of here, these people seemed able to derive entertainment and fun from any event or activity. Life was for enjoying.

When we came back to the village again, Nkwanu Knaii had returned and was talking to a tall, gaunt man dressed in skins. I was not introduced but noticed that this man watched me closely and listened intently to everything that was said. Ekwona described our visit to Gijeni in great detail and said he wanted to do something similar for Inkwiti.

Nkwanu Knaii explained my problem with living on the far side of the town and the time it took getting from there to the forest villages. Then he asked if I might be allowed to stay in the village occasionally when work brought me here.

Before Ekwona could answer the gaunt man leaned across and said something to him in a low voice. The headman first looked surprised then pleased, turning back to us with a broad smile. "Why does he live so far away?" he asked. "He should live here, in the forest."

My house at the end of the village

The Party chief looked pleased. "But you do not have any extra houses here."

"There is one at the end of the village," he waved his arm towards a crumbling ruin. "It is broken now, but we can mend it."

And so it was agreed. I would come and work with the villagers to rebuild the house and then move in. Ekwona was worried that I would find it too primitive, but the gaunt man smiled when I told him that I had spent my childhood living in a house no different and did not need electricity and modern fittings to be comfortable. I asked what I should pay for using the house but Ekwona looked scandalised. I was going to work on rebuilding it and then help them with their springs. That was worth more than payment.

I held out my hand to seal the bargain. With twinkling eyes, the headman spat on his own palm and slapped it into mine. My housing problem was solved.

Two weeks later I moved in, with the walls rebuilt, a newly laid floor of beaten clay, and a smart new thatched roof.

The night before I moved, Nkwanu Knaii and his wife invited me to their house for the evening meal. It became a full family gathering when various brothers and sisters arrived. The party went on into the early hours of the morning.

I had been a frequent visitor to his house and was often to be found crawling round their yard on my hands and knees making farmyard noises while the children climbed all over me and rode on my back. Their mother, Akanku, had become like a favourite sister and was a valuable source of information, comment and advice. Her help had been invaluable to me as she talked to me only in the local dialect and she loved to talk about her beloved forest. As a teacher she was superb. To Akanku and her husband I owed a great deal, not just for their help and advice, but for the friendship that included me as part of their own family.

The following morning Nkwanu Knaii came down to Inkwiti to see me installed in my new home and was surprised by how little kit I brought with me – it comprised one bag made out of a single goat skin which held everything I owned. I told him I had all I needed.

"You will do well with these people, then," he said, "for they have as little as you and they have all they want."

Chapter 5

SINGING VOICES ANNOUNCED that some of the women were returning with their morning harvest of fruit. Abélé would be back too and I should be there.

We climbed out of the water, shook ourselves dry and dressed. The path up the riverbank to the village was short but steep and halfway up we met Abélé charging down to find us. She was laughing and excited and was being chased by several of the other village children.

The fruit collecting had evidently been successful for a large pile of fruit lay beside the door, topped by a stalk of brilliant mauve orchid blooms, each one almost as big as my hand. I picked it up and held it to my nose but it had no scent. Some of these plants gave off heady perfumes that pervaded the forest so that one could smell them several hundred yards away, but this one relied on the vividness of its bloom alone to attract pollinating insects and tiny, nectar drinking sun birds.

It was thoughtful of Abélé to have brought it and I found a bottle, filled it with water and stood the stem in it on the table.

Although it was still quite early, I knew that Nkwanu Knaii

wanted to get back to his office. He had laid aside a heavy workload to join the conference last night, but it could not be left indefinitely. Friendship could only be permitted to trespass so far and he still had his own family and his duty to the Party to attend to.

Abélé gathered a few things and was soon ready to go. She was fussing about food for me but I told her not to bother. There was still food left over from last night that I would offer my unwanted guest when he came. Other than that I could fend for myself for the few days she would be away. I told her to go and enjoy herself with Akanku and the children, and not to worry.

The sound of the Nkwanu Knaii's Toyota soon faded into the forest. I tried to turn my attention to the problem that faced me but my mind refused to focus. Instead I started to do small tasks around my home; tasks that demanded little attention themselves and would let me think. This proved to be most unsuccessful and I found myself flitting from one task to another, not completing any of them and not doing much constructive thinking either.

After an hour of fruitless activity I stopped and sat on a log in front of the house. A few minutes later, Mpwanzu ambled over and joined me.

"When I am troubled, I go and cut down a tree," he said, apropos of nothing. "The hurting in my head gives power to my blows. The relief is better than a good piss."

"I have no need of a tree," I grumbled, knowing there was sense in what he said.

"Clear the ground for the banana trees you told me you will plant. That will be hard work and give one useful result, maybe two."

"Two?"

"Your head may find the answer to what troubles you."

"Ah, you are wise, my friend. Hard work for the body frees the mind from petty concerns. I will clear the ground as you suggest. At least there will be a place to grow banana trees and the day will not be wasted."

"Do you wish me to help you?"

"Thank you, your help is welcome."

I brought out machetes, an axe and hoes and the two of us set to work on the dense scrub just behind my house. The forest had been cleared from this patch at some time in the past, probably ten or more years ago, so there were none of the giant trees that dominated elsewhere. Here the trees were only fifty or sixty feet high and a foot or two across the trunk. Before these could be reached, however, it was necessary to clear the ground cover. This was a dense tangle of vines, creepers, small bushes, spindly young saplings and fallen branches off bigger trees, piled some fifteen feet deep. Beneath all this was a thick carpet of soggy, rotting material populated by all sorts of obnoxious creepy-crawlies, many with a poisonous bite.

These were not the only hazard. The vegetation carried its own protective armoury. Some of the plants bore sharp, barbed thorns that would tangle in the fur of passing animals or lacerate unprotected skin. A number secreted a sticky sap while others were coated with a fine velvety coat of bristles that looked attractive but caused painful inflammation and rashes when inadvertently touched. In the humid forest environment, these could easily turn septic, resulting in suppurating ulcers that took months to heal. I spent a few hours every week treating villagers who had been attacked by these plants and they pursued their own traditional treatments as well. These were just a few of the daily hazards of forest life.

Such plants were, fortunately, in the minority, at least in this patch. I had wondered before about the possibility of burning it off, but the villagers said that while it was still growing it would be too damp to burn properly and would only result in the whole village being kippered. First it had to be cut back. Later it could be burned, but probably not until after the rainy season as five or six hours' rain each day kept most things too wet to burn.

So we hacked and chopped and pulled, cutting everything small and piling it in a great heap. I soon understood why the forest people did not clear more ground for planting and preferred to roam the jungle and collect what was naturally available. Clearing ground was very much harder than just hacking away enough to make a narrow passage. That, which had always seemed such hard work before, was easy compared to this.

As we worked, Mpwanzu told me about the different plants, laying some aside for later use. Most of the vines and creepers had local names, although some were probably still unclassified by botanists. The names related to their uses. Some were used for binding roof timbers together, others for making nets and traps for small animals. Several had medicinal properties to help with ailments as varied as fevers, stomach pains, swollen joints and infected cuts. Some had legendary properties comparable to Viagra, while others were used as contraceptives. I was surprised to find that many of those plants with the most vicious protection also offered the best medicines.

Some of the bushes and saplings grew tall and straight, providing good building materials, while others, when their leaves and bark were boiled, provided an insect repellent and rot proofing paste with which rafters and building poles were treated against the ravages of termites and fungus. The bark and fruit husks of one small tree could be shredded and boiled to provide a strong poison in which hunting arrows were dipped. The slightest scratch from one of these would induce a fatal heart attack in most forest animals, except for the very largest. Who needs modern technology, I wondered, when the forest provides so many useful things?

Mpwanzu's commentary provided an interesting and useful lesson. As Ekwona had promised when it was first agreed that I should live in Inkwiti, the villagers missed no opportunity to teach me about their lives and their environment. In ten months I had already learned a vast amount and continued to learn more every day.

LISTENING TO MPWANZU TALKING about how the village women derived their medicines from the forest plants gave me an additional insight into how they were valued, and I began to develop a new understanding of how I should, perhaps, be assessing the matter which now faced me. It was clear from the way he spoke that both he, and the other men, had a deep and sincere respect for the abilities of their women and that this was the foundation of their value. Only when this was truly understood could their value be related to what would be asked for them as brides.

The women were the mainstay of the labour force. While the men performed some of the more demanding physical tasks, like building houses or clearing pathways through the forest, these tended to be intermittent activities and of fairly short duration. The women did all the routine work of fetching water, fuel and food. The women cultivated the many small plots that were scattered around the village and in nearby forest clearings, and harvested their crops of yams, taro and manioc. The women washed, cleaned and cooked, bore the children and cared for them. The women made baskets, mats, string and rope from a wide selection of plants that they had to seek out and harvest from the forest. On top of all this, they performed a thousand and one other tasks that kept them constantly busy, while the men had time to sit and smoke cheroots and talk, occasionally using the string and cords their women had made to fashion hunting nets and snares. The work the men did was, on balance, a much less onerous daily burden.

Abélé was approaching fourteen years old, as near as I could estimate. She was already considered a woman in this culture and performed many of the tasks that any other woman would do. True, I made sure that she still had time to spend on more frivolous pursuits, and encouraged her pleasure in these, but her childhood was essentially behind her now. Her knowledge of the forest plants and their many uses was already very extensive. She was good at finding food in the forest and an excellent cook. She kept the house clean with the minimum of fuss and tended our small plot of vegetables with dedication that would make any British gardener admire her zeal. With nimble fingers, she fashioned beautiful baskets and mats from raffia, palm leaves, cane and grass, whenever one was needed. She was vigorous, open, friendly and keen to learn everything anyone was willing to teach her, and she did it all with a sunny smile. Having been something of an outcast from village society when I had first moved here, she was now accepted, respected and a valued member of the community. To me she was this and more; she had become, in a very real way, my daughter, and was very much loved.

How on earth, I wondered for the hundredth time, does one set a bride price for such a girl so that it will be seen to be fair and yet be beyond the willingness of the supplicant to pay?

Some time around midday, Mpwanzu's wife came looking for him with a basket of food. She had brought enough for me too, knowing that I had sent Abélé to town with Nkwanu Knaii, and I was grateful for her thoughtfulness. This, and the way the men had advised me last night, and how Mpwanzu had been subtly teaching me more than just forest lore this morning, told me a lot about the way the village people felt towards both me and Abélé. Their welcome and support, the way they helped me learn; the way they learned form me, and the fact that they had entrusted the care of one of their orphans to me, showed friendship that went far beyond mere acceptance. I felt that now I belonged and was one of them. This gave me a terrific boost of confidence for the moment when I had to face my opponent. I would do so knowing that the whole community was behind me.

Kuloni Nkese was an unwelcome intruder into my thoughts. I had sought, quite successfully, to banish him this morning by hard labour and by concentrating on the wisdom that my friend was sharing with me. But my dilemma would not go away. With every minute that passed the time crept inexorably closer when I should have to face that monster again and name the bride price he had demanded of me.

Despite the midday heat, I shivered at the thought and realised that, while I knew the things which could be asked as *ibene*, I was still no nearer to finding a solution to the central problem of how to make him drop his petition and leave us all in peace. Part of the problem was that however high I set the price, he would just abuse his position and steal whatever he wanted in order to pay it; always assuming that he accepted what I asked. That would make me just as bad as him for, effectively, I would be using him as the agent of extortion for my own gain. It would be seen as my gain too, because the bride price was always paid to and kept by the girl's father. No father would ever pass anything on to his daughter more than a few symbolic items from the bride price since this would be seen as giving it back to her husband and would greatly reduce her value and her status. It would also be an insult to the new husband for people would say that he was unable to afford a wife. It would be a poor reflection on the bride's father who was unable to find a man willing to pay a good bride price for his daughter. Shame for everyone and loss of esteem and status all round would be the only result.

WITH THESE THOUGHTS RUNNING through my mind we sat on a fallen log to eat the food Aduana had brought. As if sensing my preoccupation, Mpwanzu said nothing, curious, no doubt, to know whether I had decided the bride price, but unwilling to ask. I knew he could not ask as it would have been an intrusion on the privacy of my thoughts.

It was curious, I reflected, how these people who lived so physically close still managed to maintain this element of privacy. One was never alone in a community such as this and yet there was no sense of being crowded or lacking privacy. Your thoughts were your own until and unless you chose to share them. There were no meaningful and expectant looks from the others; they just waited patiently and never minded if you decided to keep things to yourself. This was only possible because no one would ever withhold anything that concerned others. To say nothing was not seen as being secretive, for those around you knew it meant that the matter did not directly concern them and were able to contain their otherwise insatiable curiosity. Once you did say something, however, questions would follow until everyone was satisfied that they had explored and knew all there was to know about the matter.

So we ate in comfortable, companionable silence, listening to the constant squawks, hoots, shrieks and buzz of forest life around us, enjoying the calm after our labours and before the storm that was certainly coming later with the man from Kimwamwa.

I still had no idea how I was going to answer Kuloni Nkese or how to set an honourable and fair price that he would not pay. Of one thing I was certain: under no circumstances would I allow Abélé to fall into his clutches, whatever the cost to me. If necessary I would even invoke my friendship with the President and seek his protection for her.

This was seeing ghosts where maybe there were none, I realised. Kuloni Nkese might decide he had had his fun and leave us alone, or he might simply refuse the bride price I asked and let the matter drop. Both these, however, were improbable options. His reputation was no figment of dramatic imaginations. This thinking had to stop. It was steering me into morbid thoughts which only led to submission by default. However else I might fail, I refused to fall into that pit. Picking up the machete, I attacked another dense clump of undergrowth, imagining as I hacked and slashed, that it was Kuloni Nkese's body. After a few moments Mpwanzu joined me and we worked on together for another hour.

When we stopped and surveyed the product of our labour, it seemed small enough. We had cleared a patch less than half the size of a tennis court, and all that we left standing on it were two tall straight trees with trunks about a foot thick. They rose, branchless, for almost sixty feet and were surmounted by small crowns of floppy, glossy leaves. These trees would be cut down later and their trunks, when split, would be used for the main roof beams of a new meeting-house that was planned for the village. The project had been under discussion for some time, but so far nobody had felt any urgency about realising it. As with many such projects, it awaited the right juxtaposition of need, availability of resources and the enthusiasm of the villagers to carry out the work. We also had a pile of thin sapling stems that would be ideal for rafters and a huge coil of the creeper that was normally used for binding these together. Abélé would start stripping these of their bark and leaves in a few days and reduce them to two metre lengths of tough fibrous rope. I realised Mpwanzu had been right. Our morning had not been wasted and there were at least two benefits we had derived from it.

The one I most needed, a decision, still eluded me.

I WALKED THE FEW YARDS BACK to the house, cleaned the tools and stoked the cooking fire Abélé had banked up before she left. Once the flames had caught on the new wood, I placed a large pot of water on the fire to boil for tea. Besides myself and Kuloni Nkese, there would be at least six witnesses to this afternoon's proceedings and I should have something for them to drink. If the suitor were well-favoured, I would have provided beer, but in this case it would have been a waste of good beer and I was unwilling to dignify Kuloni Nkese's suit with anything that could be construed as approval.

Five of the witnesses would be men, with the senior village wife as the sixth. That was Ekwona's wife, Akoné, who was like a wrinkled black elf. She was not really short but gave that impression because, although she was bent almost double after a lifetime of hard toil in the forest, she also had slightly pointed ears and was invariably laughing about something.

Next, I organised the space in front of my house, for the discussion would take place in the open. I dragged a couple of logs out from under the eaves at the side of the house and arranged them on the left of the open space for the witnesses to sit on. There was a thick log about two feet long which I placed beside the door. Our *kumpunu*, the heavy mortar, in which Abélé pounded flour and tubers, I turned upside down and positioned on a grass mat in front of the doorway. This signified that entry was denied to my house until I removed the obstacle. It would also serve as a seat for me during the meeting. Six feet in front of this I placed a clean palm leaf mat. Here Kuloni Nkese would sit, alone and at my feet, the supplicant on view to everyone.

I found a collection of old enamel mugs behind the curtain in the back corner of the house and put them by the fire. A small packet of tea and about a pound of sugar went into the water which was warming slowly and I stirred it for a moment. Abélé had swept the open area in front of the house before leaving this morning and it all looked neat and tidy. She had put away her cooking pots on a rack by the wall of the house, and left eight small parcels of food, like those we had eaten the previous night, with a basket of fruit on the small table inside.

My preparations were complete and I surveyed the scene with satisfaction and wondered what to do next. If Kuloni Nkese came at the same time, as I had instructed, he would not be here for another hour or more. I decided that after all my hard work, another swim and a wash would be a good idea.

I had promised some time ago to hang a rope from one of the branches that overhung the river, so that the children could swing and play on it. This would be a good time to do that so I fetched a length of rope from the back of the Land Rover and headed down the steep path to the river. It only took a moment to tie the rope firmly in place with the end trailing in the water. The end was badly

The river swing tree

frayed so I trimmed it with my knife and spliced it back into itself to form a large loop. When I had finished the loop hung a few inches clear of the water.

News travels fast in the forest and a few minutes later, while I was washing myself on the shingle bank, the first of the village children found the rope. With shrieks of delight he swung on it and called his friends. By the time I had finished washing there were twenty small black bodies swinging on the rope and from the branch, falling in the water, all shrieking and hooting with laughter.

Chapter 6

AS I WENT BACK UP the path to my house, I met Ekwona coming down towards the river.

"What is all that noise? Are the children throwing stones at a crocodile?" he asked.

"No, I've hung a rope from the tree over the river. The children have just discovered it and are having great fun."

"You spoil them, Kamran, but it is good to hear their voices happy."

He returned to the house with me and sat down on one of the logs, looking round at my preparations as I dipped a mug of tea from the now boiling pot and gave it to him. I removed the pot from the heat and stood it beside the fire to let the tea leaves settle before I strained them off.

"The man will think he is on trial, the way you have set things out," Ekwona remarked with a grin. "You should be careful when you pull the leopard's tail that he does not turn and strike you."

"He is on trial as far as I'm concerned. It may be the only time in his life that he is ever on trial, but I want him to know it."

"Éyéee! I hope your wits are as strong as your courage. Nobody has ever won against this man. I do not like having to grieve for my friends, Kamran, so be careful."

"I will try to. Who will come to witness the bride price?"

"Myself, Olidange, Mpwanzu and the Akuamba Kau for the men; Akoné for the women."

"The Akuamba Kau? I have not seen him for many days. You said there would be six, who else will come?" I asked.

"The last will be Nkwanu Knaii, but he may not be present because he is not from this village. Will you agree to him sitting inside the house where he can hear but not be seen? I discussed it with him before he left this morning. If you agree he will leave his car behind the houses at the far end of the village."

"That is a very good idea, Ekwona. I should have thought of asking for him."

"You cannot ask," Ekwona laughed. "By our custom it is for me to choose the witnesses. It is for you to choose the bride price. The witnesses do not come to be your friends, but to hear the bride price and be sure it is just. After that we may slap your back or cry in your hair as friends, but for hearing the bride price we must be witnesses. This is why we cannot even tell you the smallest thing to ask. I will bring Nkwanu Knaii now and he can hide before that man comes." He got to his feet and strode purposefully off towards his own house, returning immediately with our friend.

With a conspiratorial wink, Nkwanu Knaii went straight into the house, touching my fingers briefly in greeting as he passed. I dipped another mug of tea from the pot and took it in to him. He was rearranging the furniture, moving the cane chair and placing a solid stool close to the wall in the deep shadow beyond the door.

"I don't want the chair," he explained. "If I moved it would creak and betray my presence. The stool is better. Thank you," he took the mug of tea from my hand. "Akanku is delighted that you sent Abélé to her. They were both laughing when I left them."

"I am glad she has Akanku to advise her like a mother and a big sister. But you know as well as I do, Nkwanu, that neither of us would ever have heard the end of it if I had not sent Abélé to her at this time. Would you have liked that?"

He looked alarmed. "A nagging wife? Oh, no! Do you think she would have done that? Ayiiié!"

"You know she would."

"Then you assuredly did the right thing sending Abélé to her, Kamran," he chuckled quietly. "Now you must go outside and leave me to wait and listen on my own. That man should not know that I am here." He pushed me towards the door, so I left him and went outside to talk to Ekwona, letting a cotton curtain fall across the open doorway.

The others were just arriving and seating themselves on the logs. I looked at them and realised that I needed another seat. The Akuamba Kau is a holy man and may not sit on the same log or mat as anyone else. I went back into the house and brought out the second stool which I set a couple of feet away but beside the witness logs.

The Akuamba Kau nodded his approval as I did this and touched the tips of his fingers to my forehead as if in benediction before taking his seat. I dipped a mug in the pot of tea and gave it to him before doing the same for the others, then sat on the inverted *kumpunu* to join in the general conversation.

I knew that no one would refer to the purpose of our meeting, and there were always plenty of other topics ripe for discussion. Ekwona told the others about the rope over the river and the fun the village children were having playing with it. The villagers always found it curious that I expended effort on behalf of the children, who were normally left to amuse themselves. This new idea provoked a lot of discussion and I could see that it wasn't only the children who would make play of it. All these people had a lively sense of fun and it took very little to turn them from more serious tasks to light-hearted diversions.

After a while the Akuamba Kau broke his silence and changed the subject. "You have been cutting down the jungle, Kamran," he observed. "Is this a new project or are you merely intent on repelling the intrusions of the forest into the village?"

"I am clearing the ground to plant banana trees. We have found some trees in the forest that give pink fruit and I want to grow them here. I will also plant peppers and other vegetables if there is space," I told him.

"You are becoming a farmer now?" He sounded amused.

"No, but when people have to search to find fruit in the forest it takes time. The plants are easy to cultivate so it makes sense to grow some near the village. Then there will be more time for other things people want to do. Also those trees we have now exposed by clearing the ground will be good for building the meeting-house we have been talking about."

"Ah, the meeting-house; it has been talked of for a long time," he nodded, knowingly. "Why do you want to do this now?"

"I know it has been talked about for a long time, but we shall soon have all the wood needed, so maybe the others will decide the time has come to do the work," I told him, noticing Ekwona and the others nodding their assent.

The Akuamba Kau looked at me and gave a small twisted smile, "There have been many changes since you came to live here. What other new things do you have in mind?"

"I don't plan to change things. What we have done is what everyone has agreed should be done. I am new here and cannot tell people to change, but if people want new things and my knowledge is useful to help them, should I not help? Nothing new has been done without everyone agreeing."

"But there are things you know should be done that others cannot see," he probed and I realised he was testing me.

"If you went to the city, could you tell people what to change?" I asked in reply.

He smiled again. "I do not know the city. How should I tell them?"

"It is the same for me here. I am like a small child in this forest, still learning its ways. My friends have always lived here and already know these things. How should I tell them to change when I know so little?"

"You teach people how to have clean water."

"But they already know they want it. I am simply helping them to provide what they know they want. Because they have chosen to do the work, they will look after the springs, even when I am not here. I only show people how."

"Yes, by using knowledge of their inner needs and seeing what they really desire, you achieve your aim. This is a skill you must remember today and use wisely."

I noticed the change in his tone and realised that he was directing my thoughts. He, like the others, was not permitted to tell me how to reply to the demand that Kuloni Nkese had made, but he was doing his best to point my thoughts at where the man might leave himself vulnerable. Indirectly he was showing me how to formulate a reply that would achieve my primary objective of safeguarding Abélé.

It occurred to me that I should perhaps have been giving more thought to Kuloni Nkese's nature and his desires, rather than just seeking obstacles to put in his path. Like a shaft of sunlight burning through the clouds, I saw the wisdom in the way this ragged witch doctor was guiding my thoughts. If only such clear sense had come to me sooner. What are Kuloni Nkese's inner needs, I wondered.

While the others carried on a vigorous conversation about village affairs, I drifted off into thought about my opponent in this distasteful business and about the man who had just set my mind on the path towards a possible solution.

Chapter 7

THE MAN KNOWN TO US ALL AS the Akuamba Kau was in a very real sense my friend, and yet I hardly knew him. He had been the gaunt skin-clad person to whom neither Ekwona nor Nkwanu Knaii had introduced me the day my move to the village had first been proposed. He had listened intently to the discussion and made several quiet comments to the headman, but said nothing to me, while watching me intently all the time.

I hadn't needed to ask who he was, for his demeanour and the deference with which he was treated, as well as his unusual garb, told me all I needed to know. I had encountered such men in other communities all over Africa and had learned to have great respect for them. Certainly some were little more than a sham, but there were many with abilities which defied the explanations of logic and who possessed an intimate understanding of the workings of the mind, displaying extraordinary skill and wisdom in the way they used this. This man, as I had good reason to know, was one of these.

A few weeks after I had moved to the village, Ekwona had warned me that I would receive a visit from the Akuamba Kau who wished to talk to me. I wondered what it was all about and worried briefly that I had unwittingly transgressed some unexplained taboo, but the headman reassured me that this was not the case. The witch doctor had simply told him that he wished to speak to me and would come when he was ready.

He didn't live in the village but was frequently there, part of the community and yet separate from it. I assumed he had a house in the forest somewhere nearby. Such men are often private in their ways. They can sometimes make others feel uncomfortable if they live amid the closeness of village society for they live more intimately with the spiritual aspect of life than the rest of us, and yet I had known others who lived in a village house just like the other members of the community. This man was exceptional. Most times he was simply there at the right moment. People were either unaware of his arrival and departure or simply paid no attention to it, accepting him as part of the normal environment.

He came to my house one evening as I was about to eat, clapping his hands softly outside the door to announce his arrival and seek admittance. It was raining quite heavily at the time, so rather than sit outside as one often did when visitors came, I invited him in. We sat on a thick grass mat and shared my food. It surprised me to notice that despite the heavy rain he was quite dry and yet I had seen no sign of any other covering than the skins he always wore, not even one of the long palm thatch hoods that were used as rain capes by the villagers.

He asked little as we ate, but talked to me about the forest, its peoples and their ways. He told me about the ancestors and the intimacy of their involvement in people's daily lives and he started building my understanding of the relevance of various customs and taboos in the social fabric of the village. He was an expert and subtle teacher, explaining complex matters simply yet with colourful and vivid illustrations. I found his presence both comfortable and reassuring, his manner dignified but in no way aloof.

After we had eaten he told me that he wished to make a reading of the signs for me. He asked where my cooking pot had come from and seemed pleased when I told him I had made it myself from clay dug out of the river bank. He instructed me to take the earthenware pot and clean it out with my own hands. I could use twigs and dry sand, but no water, as this would wash my spirit from the pot.

When I returned with the cleaned pot he had pushed my small table aside and was seated on one end of the grass mat. He bade me sit opposite him on the mat and took the pot, cradling it in his hands as if it were a precious jewel. With his eyes closed he turned the pot, exploring all over its rounded exterior with his long delicate fingers. After some minutes he placed it on the mat beside him, looked up and asked if the cooking fire was still burning. I told him it had died down but there were still plenty of hot coals among the ash.

With sinuous grace he rose and went outside, saying nothing. He returned a few moments later with a large pile of glowing charcoal cupped in both hands and seated himself on the mat as before. Raising his hands before him he blew a long steady breath on the coals until they glowed brightly, then he placed them in the cooking pot.

Taking up the pot he again, he blew on the coals until sparks flew and I could see his face reflected in the glow. Holding it out in front of him he gestured for me to take the pot. I held out my cupped hands to receive it and felt the heat of the coals through its base. It was bearable, but only just.

I made myself ignore the discomfort and sat holding the pot, waiting, as he remained with his eyes closed, breathing slowly and deeply. The coals continued to glow brightly inside the pot, their incandescence undiminished. The heat seemed to increase to the point where I felt I would soon have to put it down. Minutes passed and the pain in my palms became intense. Still the witch doctor sat with his eyes closed.

Suddenly the pain went from my hands as if a current had been turned off. I looked again into the pot where the coals continued glowing as brightly as before. I moved the pot round in my hands wondering if something had burned all the nerve endings and deprived me of feeling, but everything felt normal. I could even feel the coarseness of the clay and the faint ridges my hands had left while smoothing the surface when I made the pot a few weeks ago.

I sat still and waited.

Eventually the Akuamba Kau opened his eyes, took the pot from my hands and placed it on the mat between us. He took my hands and held them between his own, looking intently into my face. I had lit the old Tilley lamp before he arrived, but this was on the table by the wall, so the room was only dimly illuminated. It made no difference to him though, for I was in no doubt that this man's esoteric skills gave him the ability to see what he wanted to see, even in the dark.

"You have a machine that listens and then talks," he said.

I nodded, realising he was referring to the small tape recorder I had in a bag under the bed.

"Bring it and make it listen," he instructed.

I fetched the recorder, checked it had a tape in, placed it on the floor next to him and resumed my seat.

"Tell it to listen," he said, so I reached over and pressed the record button.

The Akuamba Kau began to tell me things about myself that astounded me. I had told nobody in this country any of this. Many of the things he told me were very personal and known either only to myself or a very select group of intimates. As such they have no place in this narrative but, had I not believed in his power before, there could be no doubt of it now. He talked of my childhood when I had first come to Africa and the first school I attended where, for some time, I had been the only white child. He described my family with uncanny accuracy. This was incredible: I did not even have with me a photograph of them, yet the people he described were unmistakable. He talked of my later schooling, back in Britain, and the feelings of isolation generated by being in, but never part of, the large impersonal institution that was a boys' boarding school.

His hands were in constant motion over my own, feeling each of my fingers, running over the palms and round my wrists, sometimes pressing, sometimes caressing, seeking and reading through touch. His eyes, which never left my face, were alert and full of interest, gleaming in the subdued light of the gently hissing lamp.

He talked for a long time, telling me many things that, though familiar, were dimly remembered through the passage of time. They were brought vividly back to life by his words. He told me things from the more recent past that were uncannily accurate and undeniable.

At last he let go of my hands and picked up the cooking pot again, turning it in his hands and blowing gently on the still glowing coals. It was odd, I thought, that the embers were still bright and burning apparently without being consumed.

The Akuamba Kau told me to stand up and take off my shorts. Since these were all I wore it left me standing naked on the mat in front of him. He rose and moved round me, looking closely at my body from head to toe. Stopping in front of me he touched me lightly on the left side of my chest.

"This lung will break, but a doctor will cut you and mend it," he told me. "It will be well again but after it is mended you will have the honey sickness."

Again he moved round, inspecting me closely, occasionally touching me lightly with cool fingertips. He ran his hand down my spine, pressing hard, and grunted but made no comment. After a long inspection of my legs he put a hand on each knee. "These will give pain when it is very cold," he said, then touched my left hip, "and men will damage this. It will be mended but give trouble sometimes afterwards."

He moved round me again, looking intently, but apparently seeing nothing more that required comment. As he came back in front of me, he lifted my penis with his forefinger and smiled as it swelled and rose. "Ah, you will have many children but this will only give you one daughter, no more," he said and resumed his seat, his examination complete. "Sit."

I sat and watched as he lifted the cooking pot and blew once more onto the glowing embers.

Suddenly he held the pot at arm's length. I thought he wanted me to take it again and was about to reach for it when he abruptly turned the pot over and deposited the hot coals in a pile on the mat in front of me. I was slightly alarmed at this and expected to see smoke and flames erupt, but he seemed unperturbed and sat there quietly rotating the pot in his hands, tapping on its upturned base with his thumbs. The embers just lay there in a heap, hot and glowing orange.

Turning the pot over again, he put my shorts in it and held it above the pile of coals. After some moments he removed the shorts and leaned over to peer into the pot. As he did this he started to talk again. Up to now he had been talking of the past and I could recognise and verify everything he said. Now he was talking about the future and I was glad the recorder was running for I would be able to hear his words again.

Some of his references were a bit vague or ambiguous, but I realised I could not ask for explanations since he could only tell what he saw and even he might not understand what that was. Even so, it was a startling series of revelations that held me open-mouthed and spellbound.

The Akuamba Kau paused and looked up at me.

"There is one who has already seen these things," he said, half statement, half question.

"Yes, a year ago," I answered and told him of the old woman on the fringes of the Sahara who had used her sight for me after I had helped her ancient husband nurse her through a serious bout of malaria.

He listened patiently and asked several more questions. When I had finished he asked, "Why did she not tell you more?"

"She said that she could not see beyond her own time and there would be another who would see further," I explained. "I suppose she meant that she could not see beyond her death, and she was already very old."

"She saw. It is not permitted to disclose much of what is beyond one's own life, but that one was of the Great Ones. She knew all that I can see. I see her here." He shook the pot, "You were kind to her."

"I treated her sickness, that is all."

"You listened to her words, and to the words of the old man."

"I helped her husband look after her and gave her medicine, that is all. He wanted to talk, so I listened."

"You listened with your heart as few men do. I feel this too." His pause lasted a long time. "There are trials you must face. If you listen to men's hearts, you will understand. If you listen with your heart, you will prevail. Remember this for there is one who will soon bring you trouble here because of a child."

After another long pause he replaced my shorts in the cooking pot, wiped them round the inside, then pulled them out and laid them aside once more. Warming the pot over the pile of glowing embers, he stared intently into its interior. It seemed to fill with steam that swirled around as if stirred by some invisible spoon. Tilting the pot so I too could see inside he bade me watch.

Amid the swirling steam I saw figures and faces. At first these were vague and without form, but slowly the vision coalesced and became clear. A few of the faces were familiar, people I had known a long time but had not seen recently. Most were unknown to me. There were places too: deserts, cities, mountains, strange-looking temples and green fields around villages, all interspersed with the images of people.

"These are ones who will be important later in your life," the witch doctor informed me softly as I watched. "Remember, so you will know when you meet them."

For perhaps five minutes, the images continued to appear, sometimes flowing into one another, sometimes fading into the steam before the next emerged. It was uncanny and fascinating and I stared into the pot with intense interest, not really knowing what I was seeing but fully aware that one day it might be significant.

The steam gradually evaporated from the pot and I saw no more. Laying the pot aside, the Akuamba Kau sat for a moment with his eyes closed. When next he spoke his voice sounded tired. Being a seer was a taxing and fatiguing business and he now looked drained.

"There is one in this village who has nothing but life and needs help. Will you give that help, Kamran?"

"If it is within my ability, certainly I will. Who is it and what help is needed?"

"The people will tell you when they are ready."

"Did you come here tonight to ask me this?"

"I came to understand you, Kamran. I came to meet your spirit and hear it talk. Maybe also to test you." He smiled as he made this last statement.

"And who has learned more, you or me?" I asked.

"Ah! We have both learned. Is that not also your way?"

"Yes. I am grateful," I said. "Now, will you drink some tea?"

He nodded and I rose to go and make it. Only as I reached the door did I realise that I was still naked. His inspection of my body had been a curious sort of medical examination, but I was in no doubt that is what it had been. I was not embarrassed and felt no awkwardness. These people, though they wore clothes, saw nothing shameful or smutty in nakedness. That was a Western taboo, not one of theirs. What clothing they wore was for practical purposes. In any case, it must be two in the morning now and everyone would be sleeping. Nobody would see, and if they did see they would not care.

I put water in my battered tin kettle, blew life into the remaining embers of the cooking fire, added some twigs and put the kettle on to boil. I made the tea and returned to my guest.

As I resumed my seat he picked up my shorts and dumped them on the pile of hot coals that still lay in the centre of the mat between us. With a sweep of his hand he brushed the whole lot off the mat onto the earth floor. I expected to see a large charred hole where the coals had been, but the mat was unmarked.

Was it all an illusion? No, I had felt the heat of the coals. My rational mind sought an explanation but found none. The Akuamba Kau saw the surprise on my face and smiled. Perhaps it was better simply to accept that he had done what he had done. There was no question of doubting so much of what he had told me, I knew it to be accurate, so why doubt now?

The Akuamba Kau left me just before dawn, melting into the forest in his usual manner. Some time later the headman came to see me.

"If you are going to live here it is necessary for you to be part of this village," he informed me. "The others are in the forest now digging up roots of *ebugo*. Later, when the sun reaches its peak, we will hold a ceremony and you will eat this. You should eat something now and drink plenty of water because later it will make you sick. Your stomach will need something in it to expel."

I realised that the witch doctor's visit had been more than just curiosity. I had obviously passed whatever test he was conducting and the community were now going to accept and initiate me through a ritual of their own. I had seen things like this elsewhere and they varied enormously. Some were simply symbolic and involved no risk to the initiate; others used drugs, complex rituals, physical injury and could bend the mind. The name of the plant the men were harvesting told me this could be one of the latter, for I had seen it before under different names. I had not, however, eaten it. At the very least, I was to be given a close encounter with the spirit world of the forest which all these people revered. How far this extended would only become apparent as events unfolded.

I felt simultaneously honoured and apprehensive. This could be like a dreamy cannabis session or a wild, mind-bending roller coaster with all sorts of unimagined risks at the end of it. Up to now these people had been friendly, easy going and benign, but I knew enough about the mysteries and secrets that tribal life could involve to realise there could be surprises ahead of me, not all of them pleasant. How I responded would determine my future.

The Akuamba Kau had probed my psyche, my history and my character. The villagers were now going to expose my soul, put it to their own test and judge me for themselves.

AFTER MY ALL-NIGHT EXAMINATION by the witch doctor, I was tired and should have needed sleep, but the anticipation generated by Ekwona's announcement renewed my energy, even without the drug I knew was coming. I sorted out some flour and set about preparing myself some food. As I was doing this, a couple of the village women came over with leaf-wrapped bundles. They looked at what I was cooking and their faces took on expressions of dismay as they unwrapped their bundles.

My food was put aside and they laid out the food they had brought, saying that men would either starve or poison themselves if their women did not provide the right food. Ekwona should have told me this. The *ebugo* root contains a poison and I must eat the right foods in order to protect myself from the toxin while still allowing it to free my spirit. For this reason the women always prepare special food that protects the man's body before he eats the *ebugo* root.

I asked if they had eaten the root and what effect it had. They told me that it was forbidden to women because it makes them sterile. Something different was used in female ceremonies. They would feed me until the sun was high and then the men would take over. Women did not participate in the ceremony that I was to undergo. I looked at the huge piles of food they had brought and though that I would certainly be sick if I ate all that, even without this mysterious *ebugo* root. I need not have been so concerned on that account, for as I started to eat, the women joined in and ate with me. Even so, they made sure that I consumed plenty, particularly of one stew that seemed to consist of leathery leaves and thin strips of meat, liberally anointed with fiery peppers.

Just before noon, the village men arrived and the women withdrew. They brought with them some roots that looked a little like small brown parsnips. They were about a foot long and tapered from a fat crown, about an inch and a half wide, down to a thin tap-root. Pealing them revealed a creamy flesh with a slightly aromatic smell which completely disguised their bitter taste.

Using my sharp knife, Olidange peeled the roots as they were needed, chopping them into small chunks that were then passed round for all the others to inspect before being given to me to chew. I wondered how much I would have to eat and looked at the pile of roots waiting. There were at least fifteen. My mouth was dry, as if I had been sucking alum, and I desperately needed some water to wash it down, but Ekwona said I had to eat without drinking until the drug started to take effect.

Some of the roots were soft and chewy, other were woody and difficult to get my teeth into. Olidange started cutting these smaller, almost shaving them, to help me chew. After about half an hour, I began to feel light-headed, but slowly my saliva glands returned to work and the eating became easier. I realised that I had lost some of the sensation in my mouth as my tongue didn't seem to be working properly and I was finding it difficult to talk properly. I wondered what it was doing to my stomach. On top of all the food the women had made me consume and the water I had drunk before, my poor stomach must be really distended by now, but curiously I felt no discomfort from the volume I had forced into it.

Gradually the pile diminished and I became steadily more light-headed. The light started to wane towards evening and I was still chomping on bits of root as the men kept asking me how I felt and what I saw. At some point they must have detected a significant change for they abruptly stopped feeding me the chunks of root and gave me a large gourd of water to drink.

Since the proceeding began, I had been sitting on a large log with my back to the forest. Before letting me drink they made me turn round and face the forest. The movement made my head swim. I felt as if I were falling over a long drop, but strong hands held my arms and restrained me. My earlier thirst had been forgotten hours ago, but the first taste of water brought it back. I gulped the water down, seizing the second bowl as it was offered. Four more bowls followed and were greedily swallowed before things went wrong.

My head felt as though it was on fire, my limbs would not respond and felt like jelly and then I was violently sick. It was a good thing the men had turned me to face the forest for the eruption was violent and projectile. The men continued giving me water to drink until what came out was almost as what went in. Then they stopped me drinking and went back to feeding me the *ebugo* roots.

This time they had been mashed it up with some liquid and it was presented as a paste. I was made to eat a small bowl full of this before the men picked me up and carried me over to where they had placed a log next to a hole someone had dug in the forest floor. They set me on my knees, leaning over the log and clustered round me, asking what I saw and what I felt. My mind was in turmoil by this time as the drug distorted my senses and my awareness. The hole appeared to be a bottomless abyss and my mind began to swim round as if in a whirlpool as the restraining released me. I was aware of people asking questions and my own voice answering with words I wasn't aware I even knew, and yet I knew they were the right words and my companions clearly understood them.

At the time I could make no sense of any of this, for the drug was powerful and I had obviously taken a large dose. I was aware of all the men staying very close to me even though they had let go of my arms. I learned afterwards that at least six of them were actually holding me throughout, but my senses were so distorted that I could not feel their grip. They held me as part of the ritual, not for my well-being or safety, although at one time I was aware of my arms flailing. By being in close physical contact, they were able to touch my spirit and see deeper into my soul, so they took turns to hold me while others administered the roots, the water and then the potion.

The vomiting passed and my mind continued its flight. All the while the men demanded a running commentary and I was aware of my own voice speaking.

At some point I was given a piece of fruit to eat and things changed again. What had been a crazy, psychedelic trip suddenly became dark and menacing. At the same time the kaleidoscope speeded up and images were flashing and warping faster than my mind could record them. All the time the men were asking what I saw, what I felt, what I heard.

I DON'T REMEMBER HOW IT ended as I must have passed out. I came to in darkness, aware of somebody beside me with his hand resting on my arm. It was Olidange and as soon as he realised I was awake he lit a lamp behind him, keeping me in shadow, and asked how I felt. I told him I felt as if I had fallen over a waterfall and been battered by the river. My mind was clear but I was exhausted and hungry.

He brought the light round to look at me and peered closely into my eyes, his own showing an expression of slight surprise.

"Am I all right?" I asked him.

"You went deep and travelled far with the spirits," he said. "I have not seen one go so far and yet your eyes are clear. You will have no ill effects. You are truly one of us now, Kamran."

The name was strange, but I dimly remembered being named at some time during the crazy events of my drugged initiation. I had been asked my proper name and as I recited it in full they had picked on one name which had significance for them. So they had named me Kamran.

"I did not know what to expect this morning when this began," I said. "But I am grateful to you and all the others for looking after me. I hope I did not disgrace myself, I think I was saying some wild things."

"It was not this morning. You have slept more than a whole day and a night. The further you travel, the longer you sleep," he replied. "What you said remains secret and is known only to the men of this village and to the spirits. What is important is that our spirits have seen your spirit and will always recognise you. There is no shame in this, we do not judge. Our purpose was to meet and to know. Now you are one of us."

He left me for a moment and returned with some mashed taro wrapped in a leaf. He stoked up a small fire that was smouldering in my cooking hearth and put water on to boil, dropping leaves and a few twigs into the pot. We ate and drank together and as dawn brought the light others joined us, each man patting me on the side of the neck as he arrived, each giving me a small gift of food.

"There is work to do on the spring," Ekwona announced when he arrived. "But today we will hunt. Tomorrow we work."

And so life returned to normal, only it wasn't the same. Everything seemed a little brighter, a little fresher. The forest was more vibrant and its dank, steamy atmosphere was less oppressive. The irritating insects bothered me less and I found I moved in the forest with greater fluency and ease. The people's manner assumed a subtle new familiarity and I really began to feel that I belonged in this place.

Chapter 8

AKONÉ PUSHED A MUG of tea into my hand and I became aware of a deep silence. This was odd because, even around the village, the forest was invariably noisy with croaking frogs, bird calls and the occasional chattering of monkeys in the thick canopy high overhead. Now the forest was silent and even the happy shrieks of the children down by the river had ceased. It felt as if life itself was holding its breath.

The hairs on the back of my neck stood up in alarm and I looked around. The villagers were all looking towards the point where the track to the east left the village and disappeared into the trees. As we watched, we saw the man we had all been awaiting with dread emerge from the forest and stride purposefully towards us. Following him were two men, strangers to us all, whose faces betrayed their apprehension and unwilling participation in the charade. These men must be from Kimwamwa, I thought, Kuloni Nkese's witnesses. So, for the time being at least, he was still following the customary ritual.

As they reached the open space in front of my house and stopped, the forest resumed its noise and life seemed to breathe again. I heard a soft sigh as one of my friends released pent up breath. My alarm subsided a little, but I was still on guard.

"Greetings. I have come as you commanded," Kuloni Nkese began the formal ritual required by tradition of one arriving to present his suit.

"Greetings, I am here to listen as you requested," I responded, and gestured to the mat before me, "Take your ease."

Kuloni Nkese lowered his great bulk onto the mat and our positions were reversed from yesterday's encounter. Then he had loomed menacingly over me, now he sat at my feet, as a supplicant. I noticed that someone had brought another log for his witnesses to sit on and placed it a few feet behind where he sat.

Before they took their places, each man kissed his fingers and offered his upturned hand to the Akuamba Kau who responded by brushing his own fingers lightly across the offered palms and nodding in recognition of the greeting. Kuloni Nkese ignored him.

Akoné dipped three mugs in the pot of tea. His witnesses accepted the offered mugs but Kuloni Nkese turned his head away and ignored her, so she placed the mug on the ground beside him and resumed her own seat, saying nothing of the insult.

Though I wished I could run and hide, I could delay no longer. I took a sip of my own tea and placed the mug on the ground. "Kuloni Nkese, you came to my house yesterday and asked me for something. You told me yesterday that you were content to follow the customs of the people here in this matter. Is that correct?"

"It is so," he said in a sulky tone.

"By custom I must answer you. I have given many hours of consideration to what you have asked and I am ready now to answer. As the custom demands, there are witnesses here from this village to hear my answer and see that it is just. Three are here as fathers, one as a mother, one is impartial. They are also present to hear your response. Do you understand this?"

It was evident from his reaction that the big man was uncomfortable, but he had put himself in this position by agreeing to abide by the local custom. He had even brought his own witnesses so he could not easily revoke that decision now. Inwardly I enjoyed his discomfort.

"I understand, but what do you know of the customs here, *mundele?*" he snarled. "You have chosen these men because they will think and do and say what you tell them. And what is that sorcerer doing here?" He pointed rudely at the Akuamba Kau. "Are you resorting to magic now? You are a fool and you know nothing."

"I know what is necessary, Kuloni Nkese," I said, hanging on to my temper from the inside. "As these people's custom dictates, the witnesses were not chosen by me but by the village. The Akuamba Kau has the right to be here for he is the only one in this who sees all sides. Are you afraid of what he might see in your heart that you protest like this? To call me a fool is not the way to make a good start. If this thing is to be, you would become my son. Should a father accept rudeness from his son?"

I paused and looked at him, not really expecting an answer. He just sat there with an angry expression on his face.

"You have brought your own witnesses with you as custom requires. Are these men from Kimwamwa?" I asked.

"They are from Kimwamwa," the big man replied, in better control of himself now.

"Then, if it is still your wish, you may make your formal request to me now, before all these witnesses."

"I wish to know the bride price for the girl," he responded.

"Why do you wish to know that, and for which girl?" I prodded him. "It is the custom only to name the bride price for any girl when she is sought by name as a wife. Other men have no right to ask."

"I want the girl who lives in your house, the one you call your daughter. What is her price?"

"I told you yesterday that she is not for sale like a donkey or a slave. What do you want her for?" I asked. This was like drawing teeth, and I admitted to myself that I was beginning to enjoy it equally as much as Kuloni Nkese was feeling uncomfortable. However temporarily, for I knew he was adept at intrigue, the tide was flowing my way.

"For my wife!" He spat the words at me.

"So you want a girl who lives in my house as your wife, but you do not say who the girl is. Does she not have a name?"

"You know who I mean," he snapped angrily.

"The custom requires you to name the girl you want as your wife, otherwise how can the bride price be set? So, what is the name of the girl you are asking for?"

I knew I was pulling the leopard's tail hard now and he might turn and bite, but I was determined to expose what was in this man's mind. I remembered now what the Akuamba Kau had said about listening to the voice of a man's heart. Abélé was just a pawn, an excuse, it was not her he really wanted, I felt certain. Any other man would have named the girl with respect and asked for her with humility.

It dawned on me that humility was something Kuloni Nkese could never manage. It had no place in a psyche set on dominance. He wanted to get his own way without having to pay the price himself. I began to see the basis of a fair and just bride price that he could never pay. Money he would steal or extort and pay however much I asked. But asking for money would be to use him as the agent for my own gain, and that was as unacceptable to me as it would be to the village. I still had to live and work among these people, but that would be impossible if I threw away whatever respect they had for me. Goods he would also steal, with the same result.

But respect and humility are commodities of a different sort. These came from within and could only be given by one who understands their nature; one who has them in his heart. Kuloni Nkese had no understanding of respect: he dealt in fear. He feared no one because he made everyone afraid and no-one had ever dared oppose him. Humility was alien to his nature; and he was blinded by his own arrogance and self-importance. His heart had self-interest as its core. Perhaps these would disguise my strategy until he was committed and it was too late for him to divert me.

Here were the seeds of the bride price, planted in my mind by Kuloni Nkese himself. This realisation must have shown on my face for when I glanced at the Akuamba Kau, I saw recognition in his eyes even though his face was impassive. He gave a slight nod and I felt a wave of reassurance.

Watching Kuloni Nkese sitting on the mat before me, I waited for his response.

"Abéulonako e'Bundélé, the girl who lives in your house," he said truculently, adding after a long pause, "I want her for my wife. What is her bride price?"

I could see that it had cost him a lot to keep control and make the request in this way. His use of Abélé's full name took me slightly by surprise. I hadn't even considered he might know this, but it warned me to assume nothing, to beware of everything. This man was a Party official, with access to sources of information I had no knowledge about. He was a dangerous opponent. The use of

Abélé's full name reminded me that this was not a game and I could never relax my guard.

"I hear your request, Kuloni Nkese, and I will answer you, but first I wish to know something."

He looked startled and then annoyed. He had obviously expected me just to name the price once he had made the formal request. He had not been prepared for me to question him, even though it was very much part of the custom and my right to do so. He began to look wary as I asked my first question, "Why have you chosen this girl?"

"Because I have heard of her and she will make a suitable wife."

"What is it that makes her suitable to be a wife?"

"She is a grown woman. She collects food and cooks. She keeps the house clean." He waved his arm round at the tidy space in front of the house where we were all seated. "She is of an age and needs a man to give her children. You will not do that for her, so I must do it. What is her bride price?" His impatience was barely concealed.

"You go too fast, Kuloni Nkese. I will name the bride price when I am ready. First I want to know that you truly appreciate Abélé's qualities and that you value her as I do. I warned you yesterday that you must have patience. So, how do you value her?"

"What do you mean? She is just a girl, and not married. I want her. What is her bride price?" he demanded sharply.

"Before I tell you that you must answer what I have asked. As her father, I must know that the man I give my daughter to will value her as I do; that he will care for her as I do. Unless these things are clear, how can I agree to name her bride price?"

I could see that his patience was not going to last much longer, but there was no going back now. The local custom required the prospective husband to declare himself openly and for the bride's father to be satisfied. If the petitioner failed to present his suit in the best light, it was up to the father to ask questions until he was satisfied. I fully intended to exploit this as a means of disclosing, if I could, Kuloni Nkese's underlying motives. Somehow I had to continue drawing things out until I had found the means of denying him anything to do with Abélé.

"Yesterday," I reminded him, "you told me that you wished to follow the local custom in this matter. Today, before these witnesses, you have told me this again. This custom allows me to ask questions and to satisfy myself about you and about how you will treat my daughter. You are obliged to answer if you want my agreement. You may withdraw now if you wish, in which case you may never speak to or come near Abélé from this time on. If you wish to continue with your suit, you will answer me. That is the custom."

"You are a fool, *mundele!*" He spat the words at me. "I agreed to follow the custom as an amusement, but you know nothing of this. Do not try my patience too far or you and the girl will regret it. What is the bride price?" he snarled, rocking forward where he sat, as if he was about to stand up.

"You are mistaken, Kuloni Nkese. I know and understand the custom very well and I am resolved to abide by it. But, since you are so impatient I will have to teach you what is required of you in this matter."

"You will teach me nothing. Bring the girl here and tell me what you want for her. Let that be an end of your fooling around." He hawked and spat on the ground just in front of me. Tossing his head impatiently he moved to stand up.

"Sit down!" I snapped. "You asked to follow this process. I did not invite you. So be quiet and listen. I will tell you my bride price."

He subsided, more because he was taken aback at my sharpness than through willingness to behave in a civil manner.

Addressing myself to the witnesses I said: "I am asked by Kuloni Nkese, resident of Kimwamwa, for my daughter Abéulonako e'Bundélé who, in this village is called Abélé, to become his wife. He has stated before these witnesses his wish and intention to follow the custom of her people in this matter and has offered to pay the bride price set by her father. This is the *ibene* that I set for my daughter."

"Get on with it," my would-be son-in-law snarled petulantly from his mat. He was becoming nervous, not just because I was spinning things out, but because he had finally realised that I was indeed familiar with the customs and traditions of this matter and he had assumed I would not be. I had shaken, at least slightly, his belief in his own infallibility.

"The *ibene* is in three parts which must all be paid in full before you may ever speak with my daughter or approach her. All three parts must be paid in full within three months of today, which is two days after the appearance of the new moon. If all these conditions are not met, any part which has been paid will be forfeit and you may never approach or speak to my daughter for any reason or in any capacity. These are the normal conditions which are traditionally imposed in this community and may not be varied." I looked at my witnesses and saw them nod in agreement. Kuloni Nkese's witnesses were also nodding.

Turning back to him, I continued. "The first part of the bride price for my daughter relates to land and housing that is required. The second part relates to goods that you must provide for my daughter's use and benefit. The third, and most important part of the bride price, relates to the duty that must be paid to Abélé's father, the elders, the ancestors and the spirits. These three divisions are also part of the tradition of this community."

I looked again at my village friends and saw them nodding their agreement. Kuloni Nkese was looking down at the mat on which he sat, with a sour expression on his face. This bully, normally so big and sure of himself, was trapped by his own arrogance and he knew it. Even so, he must be plotting some form of revenge. I knew that I would have to be very careful, to tie him with the intricate bonds of custom and tradition, and yet be seen to be totally fair and without prejudice. This was particularly difficult in view of the fact that I most certainly was prejudiced against him. It was my actions, however, not my thoughts that would be judged.

"For the first part of the bride price, you are required to clear and reclaim from the forest, by your own efforts, a piece of land in the village where you live to the measurement of twenty *sabakwe*. On that land you must build a house with two rooms, each of five *sabakwe*, and a covered cooking place. You may use tin or thatch for the roof, as you choose, and you may have paid help to build the house, although you must also work on it yourself. The remainder of the cleared land, not covered by the house, must be cultivated and planted with yams, tomatoes and pili-pili. You must do this cultivation work yourself and without help. This is the first part of the bride price for my daughter, to be completed and inspected by myself and these witnesses within the allowed time."

I paused and looked into the eyes of the man who sat before me. I saw his anger and braced myself for his response.

"What is all this nonsense of land measuring so many *sabakwe*? You are talking childish riddles. If you wish to play with me like this, you will regret it," he snarled.

"There is no riddle, Kuloni Nkese. You chose to follow the local tradition in this matter. I asked you before if you had the knowledge and the patience. *Sabakwe* is a traditional measure of space used in these parts when discussing the exchange of land or housing, or as part of a bride price. It is the correct form of expression for what we are discussing now. You should know this and understand it well, for *sabakwe* is a measurement related to your own size. Your impatience and bad temper do you no credit." I stared hard at him, leaning forward slightly. He glared back in silence.

"For the second part of the bride price you are required to provide goods so that the bride may be properly dressed and equipped for her new life. In addition, since you live elsewhere and would be taking her from the village of her family you must compensate this community for the loss of an able working woman. For this village, you must provide three gold five-franc coins, to be presented to the village in the traditional manner one full moon before the date on which your bride is to be delivered to you." I looked at Ekwona and saw him smile. "For Abélé you must provide a new tin trunk with two brass padlocks, so that she may keep her clothes and property safely; also two lengths of printed cotton cloth called *ikende*, and one length of plain cloth; also a packet of sewing needles and a new reel of cotton thread. You will buy her two metal cooking pots of good quality, with a capacity of not less than five *oukwe* each. You will also provide her with one new work knife and a new machete of good quality. These goods are to be delivered here no later than the full moon before the date on which your bride is to be given to you. This is the second part of the bride price for my daughter, to be delivered here and inspected by myself and these witnesses within the allowed time."

I paused and picked up my mug. It was empty and as I moved to fill it, Ekwona took the mug from my hand and passed it to his wife, who refilled and returned it. She moved among the others replenishing their tea and receiving quiet words of thanks from the two men from Kimwamwa. Kuloni Nkese ignored her and rudely turned his head away again. Akoné filled his mug without comment and returned to her seat.

I resumed my declaration of the bride price, coming now to the most difficult part; the part that I hoped would put an end to this whole unhappy charade and also protect Abélé from the man's attentions in the future.

Up to this stage, I had not really considered the need to protect myself as well, but it now occurred to me that this could be more important. Abélé was not the point; I was. If she had not been there, he would have found some other way to involve himself in my life and make his sport with me. All this business about wanting a wife was nothing more than a convenient means of embroiling me in something he thought I, as a foreigner, would not be able to understand; a means of causing animosity between myself and the people I lived among; a means of creating the strife and turmoil, the fear and terror that would gratify his warped and monstrous ego.

Until now I had been groping about in a long, stygian black tunnel. Now, at last I began to sense a way forward, as if becoming aware for the first time of a steadily growing light in the distance. Perhaps this tunnel would have an end after all. Kuloni Nkese had sown the very seeds of my enlightenment himself. It was not what he was trying to do that was important, I realised, but why he wanted to do it. His motivation was the seed of his own undoing. Its germination was the cue to my awakening, the beginning of my understanding and the doorway to my salvation. I was aware of the shackles that lay in my hands, ready to be locked about him. Not ropes or chains nor metal bonds these, but the subtle restraints of the psyche, to be wound in a complex web of interlocking strands around the fathomless blackness of his soul.

Kuloni Nkese had shown that humility and respect were the two qualities most alien to his soul. He neither possessed nor understood either. These would be the essence of the *ibene* he would never be able to pay but, I hoped, would be too proud to refuse.

Looking into his hate-filled eyes, I took a deep breath and continued. "The first two parts of the bride price are concerned with the welfare and prosperity of my daughter when she becomes a wife. She, and this village, will be the sole beneficiaries of these parts of her bride price and the fact of their payment will give her status and position in any community, regardless of the qualities and ability of her husband. The third, and most important part of the bride price for my daughter, concerns that which must be paid to me, her father, and to the elders, ancestors and spirits of the community from which she comes. This part of the payment establishes the worth of the husband. It displays his character and his ability to fulfil his role in society and it sets the level of respect of which he may one day become worthy. It demonstrates, by the way the payment is made, how much value the prospective husband places on his chosen bride and shows his appreciation of her qualities. By custom and tradition, what is asked in this part of *ibene* is simple, but the manner of its payment is important."

I was laying it on a bit thick, and could see my friends smiling as they watched Kuloni Nkese sit sullenly before me. They knew that what had already been asked was little enough to have been paid by any village man. For a man with the power and position of a Party agent, this was a small price. The expression on all their faces showed that they expected the third element of the bride price would compensate for this. Even the witch doctor was wetting his lips in anticipation.

"Is it right that a father should expect to be treated with respect and consideration by his children?" I asked Kuloni Nkese.

"It is right," he mumbled reluctantly after a long pause.

"Is it right that a woman should expect her husband to appreciate her, to value her contribution to his family, and to treat her in a manner that is respectful of her status?"

The big man remained silent, staring at the mat between us.

"Is it right?" I asked again.

"It is right."

"Then, Kuloni Nkese, as the third element of *ibene* for my daughter, I require that you shall demonstrate these things by your actions, not only here, before me and these witnesses, but before everyone in this community and the village in which you live."

I rose from my seat on the upturned mortar and brought the leaf wrapped parcels of food that Abélé had left ready, giving one to each of the witnesses and the last to the big Party agent from Kimwamwa. "Eat the food that my daughter had prepared and see that it is good. Appreciate her ability to gather and prepare food," I told them all, and resumed my seat.

"For the third part of *ibene* for my daughter I require that you, Kuloni Nkese, shall bring clay from the river and fashion two *akwali* pots, each with a close fitting wooden lid, and each with a capacity of at least fifteen *oukwe*. You shall do this work with your own hands, here, in front of my house. You will bring wood for burning and bake the pots in a fire beside my cooking fire for two full days until they are cured and ready for use. On the day that I deliver my daughter to her new home, I will bury these pots outside her doorway as a sign of my blessing and to provide cool water storage for her house."

I saw the look of astonishment creep across the big man's face as he understood what I had asked, and continued, "A wife must prepare food for her family and will work hard to do so. Even so she must have a *kumpunu* to pound flour and yams. There is a large log there beside my house. I require that you, Kuloni Nkese, shall hollow out one end of that log with tools and with fire. When this has been done you will bring gravel and sharp sand from the river to scour and smooth the inside, to burnish and polish the surface of the wood, and make a *kumpunu* big enough for pounding four *kubula* of grain or yams at one time. You will decorate the outside of the log with carvings in the manner traditional in these parts. You will also bring a seasoned hardwood log from the forest and make a new *nktuna* to be used with this *kumpunu*. This work you will do with your own hands, here in front of my house. The quality of the work and the way in which it is carried out will signify the respect you have for my daughter and her qualities as a wife and provider of food. On the day that I deliver my daughter to her new home, she will bring this with her and use it thereafter to prepare the food of her household."

I watched the big man scowl and the amazement in his eyes deepen, but he still said nothing so I carried on. "It is customary to present the bride's father with raffia mats as a token compensation for the mats his daughter will no longer make for him. The number of these mats is related to the worth and age of the bride. I require that you, Kuloni Nkese, shall come to this place and collect raffia from the leaves of the six palm trees that surround this house. You will prepare and dry the fibres and then weave, with your own hands and without assistance, six mats of the size and style known here as *ikobio*. You will do all of this work here, sitting on the mat where you now sit, both to demonstrate your skill and to show the proper respect of a son for his father because, if this thing is to be, I will become your father. On the day that I bring my daughter to her new home I will place one of these *ikobio* in the roof of the house to show that the respect is returned and to confer my blessing on her new home."

I had paused after each of the previous items, but this time I did not wait. "When a father gives his daughter as a wife, his heart longs for her to have a child of her own. It is then the father's delight to play with his daughter's child. When the grandfather is not there, the child needs toys of his own to amuse him. There is a second, smaller log beside my house. You, Kuloni Nkese, will take this log and carve from its wood a toy suitable for a first-born child. You will do this work here, in front of my house, with your own hands, and you will decorate the carving with bright colours. The quality of your work and the brightness of the colours will demonstrate the respect you have for your new father and the future you offer for his grandchildren. On the day that my daughter's first child is one month old, I will bring this toy as a sign of the bond between the generations and of my blessing for the mother who bore the child."

Now I paused and looked at Kuloni Nkese. His face was blank and he looked at me with dull eyes. This was evidently not what he had been expecting. I was almost finished now, but he did not yet know that, and I thought he looked somewhat bored, as though he had been obliged to sit through a tedious recitation and had not really been listening.

"These four tasks are the third and final part of the *ibene* that I require you, Kuloni Nkese, to pay for my daughter Abélé. They must all be completed and confirmed by these witnesses in the time already stated. If any one of the tasks is not completed, or is performed in a manner that is not acceptable, then all that has already been paid will be forfeit. In that case you will be forbidden ever to speak to or approach my daughter or even to come to this village. Then the children and women of this village may throw stones and sticks at you if you ever come here again. This is the custom and tradition that you have chosen, in front of these witnesses, to uphold. The custom now requires that you state your acceptance or refusal of this bride price. If you remain silent it will be taken as a sign that you accept and agree to pay what is asked in the manner specified."

I sat back and waited. There was a long silence and even the background noises of the forest seemed muted. I noticed that the light was fading now and realised we had been sitting there for several hours.

At last the big man stirred and for all his bulk, moved with surprising fluidity as he stood and faced me. The look on his face was of pure hatred and I realised that the true meaning of what I had asked was finally becoming clear to him. He knew that everything I had asked was within the custom of these people and that I could legitimately have asked so much more. There was nothing he could object to that would justify refusal and yet there was no way his ego would allow him to accept.

With deliberate power, Kuloni Nkese hawked and spat a huge dollop of spittle onto the ground by my feet. The intended insult was obvious but he was clever enough to ensure that his missile did not touch me and provoke a rebuke. He got one anyway.

"Kuloni Nkese, your manner does you no credit. You will have to improve your behaviour if this thing is ever to be. No father could give his daughter to be the wife of a man who has no respect. You came here seeking to ensnare me and make a fool of me, but you have found that I am not as stupid as you assumed. You diminish yourself in front of these witnesses if you cannot accept your mistake with some dignity. Now, do you accept my price?"

"You know nothing, *mundele*," he snarled, and I noticed him flexing his hands. "You talk in riddles of childish rubbish, demanding play-things for babies, pots and land measured in nonsense measures. You ask for nothing of value but three gold coins. Pwah! I can pay many times this and you know it, yet you ask nothing but nonsense, claiming it as tradition, with these witnesses nodding like a band of tame monkeys. What do you know of tradition, white man? You insult the girl by asking so little for her. You know who I am and that I can pay a proper bride price. You insult me too by asking so little. You are a fool, white man."

"You may think the bride price small, Kuloni Nkese, but it is fair. I know who you are and that you can pay a lot in goods or money, but can you pay the price that is asked? You came here with a demand that I name *ibene* for my daughter and I have done so. You claimed that you wished to follow the local custom in this matter and I have complied. But throughout you have been rude, abusive and too stupid to see that the price has nothing to do with the value of goods. You have heard what is asked. Go home and think about this. You will come here again one week from today and give me your answer. Until that time you may not speak to or approach my daughter for any reason, nor may you remain here or visit this village until you come to give your answer. Now, go."

The big man stood and stared at me, seething internally and saying nothing. After a few moments, he spat again at my feet, then strode off angrily, took the path to the east and disappeared into the forest. The two men from Kimwamwa remained where they sat, eating the food they had been given. I went into the house and fetched beer, opening the bottles and passing them round. Nkwanu Knaii came out and joined us, greeting the two visitors warmly. They were obviously well-known to him and seemed not the least surprised at his presence.

I returned to my seat on the upturned mortar and asked, "You have all heard the bride price that I set. I have tried to keep within the custom as I have learned it from everybody in this village. I believe that what I have asked is fair. Do you agree?"

"It is fair," Ekwona said, "but you have asked very little. A man in his position could be asked to pay much more."

"Some may say that you have not valued Abélé highly enough," Mpwanzu suggested, and the others nodded their agreement. "If he were a village man, it would be a very good price and would give her status in the village, but he is an important official. Her status will now depend on his position. This is not always good for a wife, unless her husband is well respected. This man is hated and feared."

The men from Kimwamwa agreed and said there was nobody in their village who liked him. I wondered how he had persuaded them to come and witness the bride price, but decided not to embarrass them by asking.

"But I have no intention of her ever becoming that man's wife," I replied. "I would not have him for a son, and will certainly never let him take Abélé."

"How can you stop him?" Ekwona asked. "You have named the bride price that any man in the village could pay."

"But he won't."

"Why not? It is little enough."

The Akuamba Kau coughed and lifted his hand. "Kamran is

right. The true bride price is not in the value of goods he has asked for. He has listened to the man's heart and asked a price of the heart he cannot pay."

"What is this mysterious price?" Olidange asked.

Nkwanu Knaii laughed and joined the discussion. "It is no mystery, you all heard it, just as I did. The goods Kamran has asked for are clearly understood and would be fair for any man from either this village or from Kimwamwa. But he also told of the manner in which *ibene* is to be paid. None of us would find this difficult, but can you imagine that man clearing the jungle, tilling the soil and planting yams, or making *akwali*. Can you see him sitting at Kamran's feet weaving *ikobio*, or carving a *kumpunu* and *nktuna* for a woman to use pounding flour and yams? He will think he is far too important to do tasks like these. That is the true price. It has been cleverly set. Maybe even now the man has not realised the full extent of what has been demanded."

"Éyéee!" one of the Kimwamwa men said. "It is indeed a very fitting price. That man cannot possibly pay it. He is too proud and important to pay such a price. It was well set."

As their understanding took shape, the others all agreed that Kuloni Nkese would never agree to pay the *ibene* I had named. The mood of the little gathering lightened immediately and assumed almost a party air.

Seeing that Kuloni Nkese had left, other people from the village began to drift over and join the conversation. I brought out the last of the beer and passed it round as the newcomers were told the news. They received it with wide-eyed amazement, then mirth. It seemed that my friends would judge me kindly for the bride price I had set. Nobody asked what I would do if the man accepted the price.

Sitting listening to their chatter, I became aware again of the shrill cries of the village children down by the river, playing with their new swing. The usual forest noises had resumed as well. For the time being at least, village life had returned to normal.

The Akuamba Kau laid his hand gently on my arm. "It was well set, Kamran. It will work out the way you intended, but there may be more trouble before it is finished. I will be here when I am needed," he said and, unnoticed by everyone else, quietly walked off through the village.

The party began to break up now and Nkwanu Knaii asked me to come back to the town with him. "You will want to talk to Abélé, so stay at my house tonight. Akanku will also want to hear it from you."

I agreed, but instead of going with him I said I would bring the Land Rover so that we could return to the village without imposing on him.

As they took their leave, one of the Kimwamwa men warned me, "Beware of Kuloni Nkese. You have challenged him. When he understands this, there will be no forgiveness in him."

Chapter 9

AKANKU HAD DONE A GOOD job keeping Abélé's mind off what was happening in the village, but both their faces showed great relief when I arrived. Rushing out to meet me, followed by a tail of smaller children, all shouting and laughing, Abélé flung her arms around me and hung on tightly. I held her close for a moment while the other children clamoured for attention, then we went into the compound.

"So, the monster did not eat you," Akanku laughed.

"No chance. Once I understood what he was doing, it was not so bad, and I had some very good advice from my friends. It's not finished yet, but I believe it will work out all right." I sat on a log with my arm round Abélé as the other children made their usual noisy greetings and a few minutes later Nkwanu Knaii arrived from his office. Then it was time to talk.

Carefully I explained again to Abélé why I had been obliged to set *ibene*, even though I had promised her she would never be given to Kuloni Nkese. Akanku had prepared the ground well for Abélé understood this and her only worry was how I was to set a price the man would refuse to pay. I found myself explaining about the kind of man I believed him to be and what sort of demands he would refuse; how he would treat with derision any demand for goods or money, but would falter over a price that required humility, respect and subordination of his own self-importance. His demand really had nothing to do with Abélé, apart from the fact that he was a full-blooded male who would take his pleasure with any woman or girl for as long as it amused him, then discard her like an empty fruit peel. His real aim was to make my life a tangle of uncomfortable complications; to amuse himself by wielding his power over me. I suspected some of his experiences in Russia back in the late 1960s had filled him with resentments, particularly against white people. So he saw me as an easy target, out of my own cultural environment, alone and without allies. If this was the case, he had blinded himself by his own arrogance and badly misjudged both me and all my friends. This was my environment and my friends in the village had made sure of this with their *ebugo* initiation ceremony.

Abélé looked horrified at what I had said and clung to me even tighter, only relaxing a little when both I and Nkwanu Knaii reassured her that we would never let him win. Her alarm gave me a new understanding of her dependence on me, and the place that I held in her life.

From the reserved, tentative child who had been given into my care only a few short months ago she had adopted me totally as her father and given me complete trust. She had made me her safe anchorage after a confusing and disrupted time adrift on a turbulent sea of deprivation, rejection and inconstancy. I was tremendously flattered by this realisation, but also slightly awed by the responsibility. Caring for a child had been one thing, but she was now a young woman emerging into adulthood with all the complications that brings. I used to think that in comparison to Western society, the forest people had less complications in their adolescent years, but the longer I lived here and the more involved I became, the more I realised the reverse is true. On top of which, at twenty-seven, I was only just over twelve years older than Abélé myself.

I explained how I had structured the bride price so that it appeared to be very little but in reality demanded more than Kuloni Nkese could give. Just as I had for the villagers, I explained how I had translated Abélé's value not as material goods, but in terms of respect, duty and service and how the manner of giving these would truly reflect the value the man placed on his prospective bride.

Abélé still seemed a little puzzled, even after I had gone through it a second time, but Akanku finally helped her understand. "Why do you make food and keep house for Kamran, Abélé?" she asked.

"Because it is my home and that is my work."

"And do you like doing these things?"

"Of course."

"Why?"

"Because Papa is special. He teaches me and does many things for me. I do these things for him." Abélé grinned at me. "I would do anything."

Akanku nodded her agreement. "It is the same for me with Nkwanu. The reason why someone is special is their true value. The more someone will do for them, the greater their value."

"Éyé! I am rich and so is Papa," Abélé laughed.

"How so?" Akanku asked.

"Because Papa would do anything for me, even if I do not ask it, and I would for him."

"Then you understand the nature of value and how much

Kamran demanded for you," Nkwanu said gently. "Do you understand why the man will never agree?"

Abélé's eyes twinkled with amusement. "He thinks he is too important to make *akwali* and *ikobio* and he does not like Papa because everyone in the forest is his friend. He does not understand that Papa is not like the old *colons*, he is like us." Her face clouded. "But won't that man be angry when he understands the price? Then he will make more trouble. We have all heard the stories about him. How will this stop him doing bad things to us?"

"He has caught himself in his own intrigue," Nkwanu told her. "He has insisted all along that this should be done according to custom and tradition. When he refuses the bride price, which all the witnesses have agreed is fair, he will be forbidden ever to speak to you. If he comes to the village the women and children may throw stones and sticks at him and drive him away. If he said he accepted the bride price and then failed to pay it properly, his shame would be even greater. Again he would be driven out. If he tries to make any trouble in the village, I will hear of it. Then I can do something official. He is a Party agent, but he has no business here and no authority to do anything in this sector without my approval. That is something he will never have."

Abélé looked at him for a moment after he finished speaking, as though deep in thought, then her face cleared and she jumped up, grinning. "It is finished, then. We have been preparing food. Now you must eat and we will forget that man." She headed towards the cooking fire. "I have been to the market and brought beer for you," she called over her shoulder returning a few moments later with two cold bottles which she opened and presented to us with a proud grin.

Accepting these, my friend and I looked at one another in

amazement. Could Abélé really shrug off something so dangerous with such casual ease? I worried that her confidence was misplaced, or at least premature, as I could not imagine Kuloni Nkese giving up easily. Nkwanu Knaii's face told me he had similar misgivings. He nodded and sucked on his beer bottle, indicating that it would be better to say nothing more for the moment. I agreed and took a pull at my own.

The two women brought food and placed it on the rough courtyard table that Akanku's brother had made for them some months ago. Then we all sat around the table and talked generally over supper. When we had finished, Abélé got up to wash the smaller children's faces and the pots and plates. Akanku stayed at the table with her husband and me.

"I have been talking to Abélé about the duties of a woman and a wife," she told us. "The village women have already told her some of these things, but I think they were not easy with the telling because of Abélé's past and her origins. She says there are some who think she is a sorcerer like her mother. They have said that is why this evil man came to seek her as his bride. He wishes to use her powers for his own evil. If that is so they may be afraid of her for this."

We digested this piece of news for a moment, then I asked "Did someone tell Abélé they thought she was a sorcerer?"

"No, she overheard two of the older women gossiping in the forest when they were out collecting fruit. She says it is silly and her mother never taught her anything about her craft."

"Even so," I said, "you must admit she's a fast learner. I seldom have to tell her anything twice. She is also becoming quite good at reading and writing and her French is workable. Few of the village women understand more than a few words of greeting and none of them are literate. They're simple folk with many taboos and superstitions who might be suspicious of this."

"Indeed," Akanku agreed. "Also she has considerable skill with plants for healing and cooking as well as their more practical uses. She must have learned this from her mother, when she was still alive, without ever being taught. That would be enough for the more traditional women to chatter about."

"All this may be so," Nkwanu offered. "But those who practice the esoteric arts are secretive and evasive, surrounding themselves with an aura of mystery. Abélé is an open child without guile or subterfuge. Everyone can see that."

"Maybe they can," I said, "but that won't stop some tongues wagging. There are those in every village whose delight is in seeming to know things others do not; who spread alarming rumours, just to see what reaction they can provoke. Old women with not enough to fill their minds quite often resort to this. The attention they get for it makes them feel important, in an exciting way not provided by other social activities. This is a normal part of human behaviour equally among simple forest folk as among the spiteful old hags I've met in my own country."

"Then what can you do?" Nkwanu asked.

"I don't know. This is the first I have heard of it, and I am not really sure if it's more than a temporary problem. If Kuloni Nkese goes away and leaves us in peace, it may just die down. On the other hand, if he really did come asking for her because he believes she has powers to help him in some perverted plan of his own, things could be far from over."

"Éyéee! This we can do without," Nkwanu sighed.

"Well, all I can do for now is keep my eyes and ears open around the village. I might talk to Ekwona about it."

Akanku snorted and looked at each of us in turn. "Both your brains are addled. The person you should talk to is the Akuamba Kau."

Nkwanu looked at me with mock horror. "Aiiié! I also married a witch! She knows all the answers to life's most difficult puzzles." He ducked as his wife swung her arm at him and banged his head on the table. "See! She makes me crack my head!"

"So! That is what you get for teasing me," she laughed.

Our discussion had to stop there as one of Akanku's brothers arrived and was soon followed by the other with his wife and elder son. We all moved inside to avoid the rain which started as darkness fell, and the evening turned into a family gathering with a great deal of news to be exchanged and several gourds of palm wine to be shared. Akanku produced more food for her brothers. It was a most convivial time and just what Nkwanu, Abélé and I needed to take our minds off the afternoon's events.

In the corner of the courtyard was a clear area covered by a thatched awning where people could sleep outside if it was particularly hot, or when too many were staying for all to sleep inside. Some time after midnight I saw Abélé go over there and unroll a large bundle of grass mats, laying them out under the thatch. The next time I looked in that direction she was curled up in the corner, sleeping soundly. Some time later Goroumi, Akanku's younger brother, and his son went off to their own home in the town. Emoro, the other brother, decided to stay since he lived further away and would not be back before daylight even if he set off immediately.

Emoro and I retired to the mats under the thatch while Akanku picked up little Admi from where he had fallen asleep under the table, and the household settled down to sleep.

Chapter 10

SLEEP CAME EASILY TO THE others, if their snores were anything to judge by. For me it was uncharacteristically elusive. I lay under the thatch listening to the sounds of the night. In the town, these were different from the forest noises I was used to. Here the incessant buzzing of a million crickets was punctuated by the occasional hoot of a night bird somewhere out beyond the sprawling houses. There was a soft counterpoint made by the minute rustlings of the small creatures that dwelt in the thatch overhead as they prowled their nocturnal domain in search of insects to devour. Surprisingly the tense exchanges of the day figured little in my thoughts, perhaps because they had been talked through to exhaustion during the evening. Abélé, however, was central and I considered again what an important factor she had become in my life.

I had seen Abélé the first time I had visited the village with Nkwanu Knaii, just over a year ago. I had noticed her particularly because she was the only child without a smile on her face. She had seemed somewhat separate from the other children. At first I thought it was because she was older than them, but this could not be so for age is no barrier in children's activities, particularly in this part of the world. I noticed her again the following day after Ekwona had brought us back from our forest trek to see the spring at Gijeni. While most of the villagers gathered close to hear what their friends had to report, the girl hovered tentatively outside the circle, cautious lest she cross some invisible boundary, uncertain and ignored by everyone. I had wondered briefly about this at the time but had little opportunity to dwell on the matter as the villagers were demanding my attention.

Soon after I had moved to the village and was installed in my new home, I received my first visit from the Akuamba Kau. Although I had been unaware of it at the time, this was to be a significant turning point in my life, for the following day the villagers initiated me into their society with that strange ritual of eating the *ebugo* roots. This confirmed my status in the village and was effectively the beginning of my association with Abélé. The witch doctor had told me that my help would be requested and a few days after my initiation, Ekwona broached the matter as we walked back through the jungle from one of the village springs It made sense that I could only be asked to take on this responsibility after I had been fully accepted by the village. My initiation was therefore very significant.

He turned off the path and led me towards a large tree where the village boys had earlier been collecting honey. Hearing the hum of bees in the canopy above, I looked up. The bees were not visible, but I realised that their hive could be a hundred feet or more above our heads. In a slight clearing – the description is purely metaphorical, for the place was no more than a slightly less dense patch of tangled undergrowth – Ekwona stopped and pointed upwards. "Our honey pots," he laughed.

Above us, where the undergrowth thinned, I could see the massive trunks of half a dozen huge trees soaring branchless towards the lofty canopy. At the point where the branches began the trunk of each tree bulged grotesquely and appeared to be covered in a gnarled warty growth. The hum of the bees was louder here and, although the insects themselves were too small to see from the ground, my eyes sensed a constant subtle movement as individuals came back laden with exotic pollen and others departed in search of more. It was something of a shock to realise that the village boys regularly climbed these huge trees to raid the six hives, risking the fury of a million protective bees every time they did so. I was not aware of anyone in the village who had been badly stung by bees, although people returned every few days with laden gourds of sticky honey. I asked Ekwona how they managed it.

"We live in the forest like the bees," was his reply. "We have learned to live together."

"But bees have a very different sort of society," I observed. "They are very protective."

"Just because things are different, or even opposites, does not mean that they cannot learn to get along together," the headman said. "The bees are simple creatures. Men make things complicated, but all we do is make them less workable. Because of that sometimes one or two lose what they have. We have a person in our village who has lost much and now owns little more than life itself. Unlike the bees, men find it hard to help one who is not of their own blood. They will give food and will not be cruel, but that is as nothing."

"Who is this, and what is the problem?"

"You have seen her," Ekwona said.

"The girl? The one who is always near the other children but never really with them? I have wondered about her. How is she so? Have her family abandoned her?"

"Her mother was one of our maidens many years ago," Ekwona explained, leaning against a fallen tree. "Three weeks after her marriage, her husband was killed by a crocodile not far from the village and she was left alone. Because of the circumstances, other people were afraid of her. They believed that to have anything to do with her would touch them with the evil spirits that had caused this thing to happen. But even though they would not drive her out she was tainted. Her life became nothing." He looked at me to see if I understood before he went on.

"When a man dies like that, it is our custom to burn his house and everything in it, to drive away the evil spirits. So Abéolu was left with nothing. She was like this for a year and three days before a man came travelling. He was *niseke* and lived in a place many days from here, up near the great river."

"*Niseke?*" I asked.

"He was a wise man. One who lived and spoke with the spirits. He came to find Abéolu and take her for his wife. The first time he came, he ignored her but simply asked to make her his wife."

"Would her father set a new bride price in such a case or would it be the same?" I asked.

"Her father was dead some years so the married men of the village decided, but the price is low for such a marriage. As you now understand, the price is related mainly to the woman's value. She had little value after such misfortune. In Abéolu's case, the bride price was half what her dead husband had paid."

"And did the man accept?"

"After making his request he retired into the forest and returned the next day, as you know is our way. The price was named and he retired again. The next day he came again and told us that the price was accepted and we should speak to Abéolu. Then he went back into the forest. The following afternoon he came again and spoke to her for the first time, asking if she objected to the marriage. Her life was destroyed and she had no future. This man's request was seen as a sign that the spirits had only been angry with the first husband and not with her. She consented because, even so, she had no other choice. The man again withdrew into the forest. On the fifth day he came again and paid the bride price. He took Abéolu back to his home the same day."

"Was there no ceremony, no wedding feast?" I asked.

"When such a man takes a wife, who is to conduct a ceremony? I told you he was *niseke*, and by reputation he was an exceptional man. The Akuamba Kau gave him much respect."

"Couldn't he perform the ceremony?"

"For such as he, it must be one of equal or greater rank. How can we who are not intimate with the spirits know how these things are done? As it was, the Akuamba Kau was present. But he said nothing. He only watched and nodded his agreement."

"So what has this to do with this girl in the village?" I asked.

Ekwona looked up into the trees again and smiled slightly. "After the man had taken Abéolu away some said that it was not so much her good fortune that he had come to give her a new life, but her first husband's misfortune that he had married her. They said that she was also *niseke* but had kept this hidden for mysterious reasons of her own. Because she was a woman, she had not been consulted about who would be her husband. That is our custom. Some said that she never wanted the first man and had used her power with the spirits to bring the crocodile to eat him."

"But couldn't she just have refused to become his wife?"

"She was never asked. Only if the woman is asked by her father does she have the right to refuse. Since her father was already dead, nobody asked her. She could say nothing. She was a dutiful girl and behaved as any woman should. It was Mokolu's bad luck that the spirits had conspired against him. It was only after the second man had taken Abéolu that tongues started wagging. Eventually all the talking died down. By that time it was generally believed that Abéolu had been *niseke* all along and had known the man would come from the forest for her."

Ekwona paused in his tale and pulled two small cheroots from the pouch hung round his neck. He passed one to me and lit them with a battered old petrol lighter before continuing his tale.

"After they had gone, we heard no more of her for two years. Then the Akuamba Kau told me that Abéolu had given birth to a daughter. I did not ask how he knew this. One does not ask him that sort of thing. But it was true. As you count it, that was fourteen years ago. There was some talk in the village when the birth became known, mainly among the older women who said the child also would be *niseke*."

"Does that follow? Is such power hereditary?" I asked.

"The Akuamba Kau says it is not. He said that the child was not *niseke* and no different from any other baby. But this did not still the tongues of chattering old women. Again we heard nothing for a long time and those people were forgotten. Many of the old ones who made so much talk then have now died. Memories have become thin, but have not ended. Some time ago we heard news of a new sickness in the forest. It was up near the great river. This sickness was taking people like fish take flies from the surface of the river. Whole villages were dead. In some there was not even anyone left to bury the bodies and to burn the houses of those who had died. Many were afraid the sickness would come here, but it died out and did not come close. Other matters took people's attention and nothing more was heard for a long time, until one day the Akuamba Kau arrived in the village with a young girl. Nobody knew who she was. Some said she was his acolyte, others suggested that he had taken a child wife, to reinvigorate his powers as he got older. None of this was true."

Ekwona paused again and broke off a long twig with which to scratch his back. Leaning back against his tree, he puffed a huge cloud of acrid smoke into a narrow shaft of sunlight that had found its way down through a gap in the lofty canopy. For a moment we watched the smoke writhe and swirl in the golden light, each lost in our own thoughts. I began to see where this tale was going and waited for the rest.

"That night the Akuamba Kau explained that the girl was the daughter of Abéolu and the man who had taken her away. When the disease had come to the great river her parents had worked tirelessly making herbal medicines and attending to the sick. Eventually they too had been taken by the sickness and they had both died. They only survived as long as they did because they lived deep in the forest, not in any village, and the sickness had never come to their house. It had taken them when they went to a village to help others. When they died, the girl had not known of it. She had waited patiently for their return, gathering food from the forest as usual, always expecting her parents to return. After some weeks the Akuamba Kau came and told her what had happened. He burned the house and took her with him on his journey through the forest. Eventually he brought her here."

"Why here?"

"Because her father was *niseke* he had given up his origin, but

Abéolu had a sister here at the time she went away. The Akuamba Kau brought the child here to live with her aunt."

"But after all that had happened and all that had been said, would the aunt accept her that easily?" I asked.

"The matter does not arise when the Akuamba Kau is the agent delivering the girl." Ekwona wagged a finger to show I should have known better than to ask such a question. "It made no difference anyway, for the aunt was old and had died some weeks before they came. There were no blood relatives left. Even so, the village could not refuse the Akuamba Kau's request. As custom dictates, the girl had the right to take the position her mother had before she departed. So she became part of the village but homeless. To any woman this is a heavy burden, but to a child it is worse. Nobody from this village would be cruel to her, but as a female child not far from adulthood she is likely to be ill-used. This bothers me. I have daughters of my own."

Ekwona fell silent, staring into the deep forest, lost in thought.

"So what will become of the girl now?" I asked after a while.

Ekwona gave me a penetrating look. "That is what I want to ask you."

"Me?"

"Without a home, her life will be less than that of her unfortunate mother after Moloku was eaten by the crocodile. The suspicion and fear that existed then is not yet forgotten. None of the village people can ever offer her a home and a family. She has no status. Without status she will never even be sought as a wife by any of the village men. Tradition and *ewo* would prevent it. We are simple people. We live in a world with many mysteries beyond our comprehension, so we are subject to all the doubts and fears and imaginings that the mind can produce. At the same time we are easily satisfied and accept the explanations and influence of those who have knowledge. This child has lived homeless among us for almost half a year. She will soon become a woman, but has neither a mother nor aunts to guide her transition. You understand why none of the village women is willing to take on this role. The girl needs a proper home and a parent who has the respect of the people. Without this she is lost. Our village will become tainted and exposed to the influence of all sorts of evil spirits."

It was now becoming clear where this was leading. Nobody in the village could take this on, but I could. Ekwona was suggesting that my status would give the child a place in the village and its life. This was the help that the Akuamba Kau had said would be sought. As directly as custom permitted, until I made an offer, Ekwona was asking for help, not just for the girl, but for everyone in his village.

Since coming here I had faced all manner of tests and somehow managed to satisfy the villagers and their complicated customs. They had demonstrated their acceptance by the ritual of feeding me with *ebugo* roots. Now it was payback time. This was more than just another test. This was judgement day.

I moved across the small clearing and pulled an unfamiliar fruit from a vine that straggled through the undergrowth. Holding it out to Ekwona, I asked, "Is this edible?"

"Yes," he replied with a slight lift at the corner of his mouth.

I took out my knife and cut the fruit in half. "Then share it with me as you are sharing your problem. Help me eat it as I will try to help you eat this problem."

His wizened face split into a wide grin as he took the fruit, kissed it and held it above his head, squeezing so that a few drops of its juice fell onto his almost shaven head. "You know this fruit?" he asked.

"I have never seen it before."

He lifted one eyebrow and looked at me for a moment with his head cocked on one side.

"Éyéee! If the Akuamba Kau had not told me it is not so, I would believe you too are *niseke*. This is *nguakua*, the fruit of understanding. If you look for it in the forest, it can never be found, but at important moments it reveals itself."

"Have you talked with the people about what you will ask me?" I enquired as he bit into the fruit.

"Indirectly," was all he would say.

I held the fruit aloft as Ekwona had done and squeezed a few drops of juice onto my hair. When I bit into it, the taste was unlike any other I had known. It seemed like a shifting mixture of every other fruit that grew in the forest and left me hungry for more, but I knew that there would be none. Ekwona watched with an expression of contentment on his face. The request had been made, the answer given; only the public formalities remained.

"Do you wish to ask me now, or should others hear it?" I suggested.

"It would be better done in the village," he said and led the way back to the path and on towards the village.

Just before we arrived, I had a sudden thought and called for him to stop. "Ekwona, I have seen this child in the village and in the forest. I know most of the people by name, but have never heard her name. How is she called?"

"You have not heard it because nobody will recognise her. They will not speak her name, so she is just called 'girl'. Her name is Abéoluneka e'Bundélé." He turned to go and I followed him into the village.

Nobody took any special interest as we passed between the

houses, and nothing seemed different from any other day. Ekwona asked me to eat with his family, so I went and sat with him on the large rock outside his house. Akoné appeared almost at once with a pot of manioc porridge and we chatted about the springs while we ate. As we finished our meal, I became aware that many of the men and all the women who were mothers had gathered around us. I looked around the faces but could not see the girl.

Ekwona looked round the gathered crowd too. "You all know the girl who lives among us and why she is not of our village. Today in the forest I have told Kamran of this problem and suggested he could help us."

"How can he? He knows nothing of this," a voice demanded from the crowd of villagers.

"Today in the forest, Kamran collected a fruit and shared it with me. This is the skin of that fruit." Ekwona reached inside his shirt and tossed the empty peel to the man who had asked. "The fruit Kamran chose is *nguakua*. That is why he can know."

The villagers looked in astonishment and the peel was passed from hand to hand. I realised that few of them had ever seen this fruit before, but its position in their mythology made them immediately accept the unfamiliar as something normal. What chance had brought this rare and special fruit to my hand, I wondered. Was it really chance? I had enough reason to believe otherwise.

Ekwona turned back to me. "This girl needs a home, Kamran. She also needs a father. Now she is a child, but soon she will be a woman. Without a home and a father she can be nothing. Will you give her these things?"

"I understand the problem, my friend. But where is the girl?" I looked around again and then saw Akoné bringing her through the throng. They stopped beside the rock where Ekwona and I were still sitting.

Ekwona turned to her and said, "Girl, you know Kamran who is of this village even if his first home was far away?" The girl nodded, her eyes wide. "He has something to ask you," the headman finished.

The girl looked confused so I climbed down from the rock and held out a hand to her. She hesitated and I motioned her to come to me. Glancing up first at Ekwona then at Akoné, she moved cautiously towards me and touched my outstretched hand with her finger tips before her eyes met mine.

"You have no family and no home," I began. "I have a fine home but no daughter to bring joy to it. Will you come and share my house like a daughter?"

Her eyes opened even wider and I saw hope blossom. She hesitated, then asked in a quiet voice: "Shall I work for you?"

"Only the work that a daughter should do for her father. Only the work that a woman does in her own home."

"Will you teach me?"

"As a father should."

"Will you teach me to read and write?" she asked, a faint touch of excitement in her voice that drew one or two disapproving clucks and muttered comments from older villagers, who thought she had no business asking so many questions when a life-saving offer had just been made to her.

I turned in their direction. "She is right to ask. It is a fool who accepts an offer with no consideration." I turned again to the girl. "I will teach you whatever I can of everything I know, including how to read and write, if you wish."

Her face gave the answer that was never spoken; she simply

reached forward, took a firm hold of my hand and moved to stand beside me. I looked at the headman and raised one eyebrow in query. Ekwona smiled and nodded so I led the way through the crowd. As we reached the edge of the gathering, I realised there was one more thing to be done and turned back.

The villagers fell silent, fearful that I had changed my mind and re-laid the burden on their shoulders.

"For this child, and for me, this is a new beginning, a new life," I said. "When a new life starts we give the child a name. Know this child as my child and that her name is Abélé." I looked down at the girl who began to laugh for the first time I had ever seen.

So I acquired a daughter, she a father, and together we went home. Some days later, when we were chatting, Abélé asked me how I had chosen her name.

"The name you had before was too long and difficult to use all the time," I said. "So I took the prettiest bits of each half and made Abélé. Also, in another place where I have been, in the language of the people there, this word means 'sunrise'. Do you like it?"

"Yes Papa!" she said, and made happiness complete.

LYING UNDER THE THATCH of Nkwanu Knaii's shelter and thinking of those strange events still gave me a tingle of excitement. It reinforced my determination that Kuloni Nkese should fail in his plot. Abélé had started her life with me as a tentative child, unaccustomed to receiving attention or love but eager to learn, as if by doing so she could secure her own future. As days passed into weeks, she became more self-assured and the other village children soon forgot their reserve and accepted her fully. Some of the older women remained wary but the younger ones, who had no direct recollection of Abélé's past, seemed to accept her well and often called for her to accompany them on food-gathering forays into the forest. I realised that some of them actively sought her company because she was really more skilled than they in the ways of the forest, despite the fact that everyone had spent all their lives there.

Within a few months Abélé had set aside her past and was behaving just like any other young girl. She had a talent for cooking as well, and between us we made our lives very comfortable and enjoyable. She was always particularly pleased when others in the village came to eat with us, for to eat another's food showed acceptance and respect that mirrored her status in society.

The mumblings and mutterings of the superstitious old crows subsided and we all got on with our lives. Each day I spent time with Abélé, teaching her all manner of things, but her greatest enthusiasm was in learning to speak French and to read and write. On her first day with me, I had written her name on a piece of wood with a stick of charcoal from the cooking fire. She treasured this and spent many hours scratching at the hard earth outside the house, copying the letters until she could form them with her eyes closed.

Three days after Abélé had moved into my house Nkwanu Knaii visited the village. I had not seen him for several weeks so we had a lot to talk about. When he arrived I was down by the river and Abélé was in front of the house pounding yams. The Party agent climbed down from his Toyota and stood watching her for a moment.

"Abélé, where is Kamran?" he asked. He told me later that she looked surprised that he had called her by name.

"Papa is down by the river," she told him, dropping the heavy *nktuna*. "I will bring him." She scampered off and bolted down the steep path to the beach where I was washing off the dirt of a hard morning's toil. Arriving breathless and excited she called me from the water. "Papa, Papa, the Party man from the town has come. He is waiting for you. Come, come now." She took my hand and pulled me towards the path.

"Slow down, Abélé. What is so urgent?" I asked, picking up my shirt.

"He is important. You must come now."

I followed her up the path and went to talk to my friend.

"So, Kamran, you now have a family of your own," was Nkwanu Knaii's greeting as I shook his hand. His face showed approval and my momentary doubt that perhaps I should have consulted him before agreeing to Ekwona's request was instantly dispelled.

"She is a good girl and needed a home," I said. "You know her history?"

"Of course. It is a good thing you have done, and don't worry that you did not speak to me first. The Akuamba Kau and Ekwona had already told me. I have come to invite you both to town, Akanku wants you to bring Abélé."

"Thank you. When d'you want us to come?"

"Now?" he laughed. "Akanku is making food."

"Then we'll come. Thank you." And so a new dimension of our friendship began.

Now, lying under his thatched roof thinking of all this once again, I realised how fast news travels in the forest. In less than three days, Nkwanu Knaii had known of the arrangement and even Abélé's new name. This last he could not possibly have been told in advance for the name had come to me only moments before it was bestowed. I was not really surprised that my friend always knew everything that went on in his sector, but I was glad that he approved of the arrangement.

I was even more pleased that Akanku had given her blessing. She and Abélé took to one another the moment they had met and Nkwanu Knaii and I were left standing and ignored as they went into the house deep in conversation. Our isolation was only momentary as the other children clustered round and demanded our attention. This was always one of the joys of visiting their house and I felt specially favoured both by their attention and their unquestioning acceptance of Abélé as if she were an elder sister. That relationship too had matured with time and this house was now a second home to both of us.

Abélé had come a long way in the ten months she had been with me, and Akanku had played a major part in her development. She had been a big sister, an aunt and a good friend. I had encouraged Abélé to come with me whenever I came to the town so that she could spend time with Akanku and her children. Whenever I arrived alone Akanku's first enquiry was for Abélé and I too received useful advice from her, not just on my own account.

From the outset Abélé had been comfortable in Nkwanu Knaii's company and listened with quiet respect to our discussions. Afterwards she often asked me about things that had been discussed and at times showed remarkable insight and understanding for one so young.

Five or six times since Abélé had come to my house, we had received visits from the Akuamba Kau. These were social visits, but I was always aware that he was keeping an eye on the situation and came as much to reassure himself that the arrangement was working well as he did to be sociable. After his second visit, he confided to me that he had come because he had been alone in the forest for a long time and was in need of a good meal. I was flattered that he found Abélé's cooking so acceptable for, although he was welcome anywhere, he seldom ate with any other family in the village. It was also a sign of his approval that did much to promote Abélé's status among the villagers, for to have the approval of such a man is something to be prized. I sometimes wondered if he was also keeping watch to see whether she had hidden abilities, but when I asked about this he dismissed the idea and said it would be better if she did not. Abélé treated him with great respect and courtesy, but was not in awe of him as some of the more simple folk were.

I found myself thinking about this enigmatic man, wondering where he lived and whether he had any family. He certainly did not have a house in the immediate environs of the village for I had come to know the forest well by this time and would at least have been aware of this. He was a wild looking man, dressed in a variety of skins, with greying hair under his leather hat. He had a porcupine quill pushed through the septum of his nose which I found odd because these animals were unknown in this region. His ears had been pierced, but he usually wore no ear rings, his only other decoration being a series of bracelets on his left arm made from braided fibres dyed in a variety of subtle colours. Once only I saw him decorated with gaudily coloured feathers, but that was much later.

Since his first visit to my house just after I came to the village, I had been aware that although he had received no formal schooling this man was wise in the ways of the world and had knowledge that reached far beyond the vast tract of forest that filled the central basin of Africa. My talks with him had been wide ranging and his insight had often surprised me. He was a major contributor to my own education in the ways of the forest and its people, and a subtle influence on my guardianship of Abélé.

My train of thought was broken as Abélé rolled over in her corner and whimpered in her sleep. I wondered if she had troubled dreams and fell to thinking about how much she might remember of earlier years. I suspected she had been happy as a small child for there was a certain buoyancy in her behaviour that could not have grown in just the few months she had been with me. I wondered if she had known other children, living in the deep forest, and whether she had accompanied her parents when they went to the villages along the great river. She seemed at ease among other people, so I guessed she was not such a stranger to others as to prefer solitude. Indeed, she was often the instigator of many of the youngsters' amusements in the village. When I had come back from the town one day with a football she had raced after it with as much enthusiasm as all the others.

One of Abélé's frequent companions, when he was in the village, was Mputu, the lad for whom I had found work in the palm oil mill down river from our village. He was a merry young man with a talent for things mechanical. He frequently spent hours tinkering with my Land Rover and I wondered if half his interest in the old machine was prompted by the attentive presence of a pretty girl. Certainly whenever he was around Abélé found reason to be nearby and the two kept up a happy chatter while continuing with their tasks. For the first time I began to wonder if there was more than his passion for machinery behind the care Mputu gave my old vehicle. Only three or four years Abélé's senior, he was bright and intelligent, and he now had a job and was bringing home a regular wage. Recently he too had asked me to teach him to read and write and had joined Abélé for lessons on the two or three evenings of the week when he was home in the village. She was more advanced in this than Mputu, and sometimes teased him about it, but it was always good-natured and it served to spur him to greater efforts. Thoughts of 'If only...' crept into my mind, but I discarded them at once because no such thing could even be dreamed of until the present dilemma had been resolved. Even so, now that the idea had implanted itself in my mind I thought it could be a good idea to encourage Mputu's interest.

Chapter 11

EVENTUALLY SLEEP MUST HAVE overtaken me for I woke to find Abélé shaking my shoulder and offering me coffee. Emoro had gone home, Akanku was feeding Admi, and Nkwanu was standing out in the early sunlight shaving in front of a small mirror. I remembered my kaleidoscope of nocturnal thoughts, but turned them aside, bringing my attention back to the present.

Abélé wanted to go to the market. She had also made a list of things Akanku needed, so we set off together on a shopping expedition. It was an enjoyable morning and we came back with laden baskets, having met a number of people we knew. Some of the village women we had met in the town gladly accepted the offer of a ride home instead of the five-hour walk with heavy baskets on their heads. They followed us back to Akanku's house like a chattering crocodile's tail.

Before we left, Abélé made Akanku promise to bring the children to visit us very soon. We piled half a dozen people and all their purchases into the back of the Land Rover and headed home. Stopping briefly at the Party office, we told Nkwanu Knaii what was happening. I thanked him for all his advice and support throughout this affair, but he brushed it aside. "You saw more than I did, and shaped the bride price well," he said. "None of us would have had the courage to challenge that man the way you did."

"You're not afraid of him!" I said with amazement.

"In my job, no. But this is different and there are influences and intrigues in which I am not as skilled as him. Perhaps sometimes it is a disadvantage to be an honest man. Even so, to deal with men like Kuloni Nkese, a man should have some fear to keep his wits awake."

We said our goodbyes and he promised to bring the family down to Inkwiti soon, reminding me of my proposal to build some sort of a raft for the children.

We arrived back in the village just before midday to find everything quiet. Most of the women were still out in the forest collecting fruit, and the men were working at the springs. It was pleasing to see that the work continued without me, even though there was a constant demand for instructions when I was there.

Olidange came out of the forest while we were unloading the Land Rover and told me that there had been no further developments and that the feeling in the village was very positive. Opinion was fully in support of the bride price I had set, once people understood the full meaning of it. Some still didn't understand, Olidange said, and he amused us by mimicking some of the clucking old women who seldom found a good word to say about anything. Later, when we were alone together, he confided that some of these had even suggested that my supposed cleverness was the product of sorcery emanating from Abélé. I was concerned by this, but apparently the Akuamba Kau had appeared among them at that moment and lashed the gossiping matrons with his tongue. He had ordered them to remain in their own houses for one full moon and not to chatter on pain of dire consequences from the guardian spirits. Olidange's description and mimicry were so funny. We shared a good laugh and felt better for it.

There was a slight breeze blowing favourably away from the village, towards the river, so Abélé and I spent the afternoon lighting bonfires on the patch of ground that had been cleared for the banana grove. Some of the village women came to take bundles of vines, sticks, or other items that would be useful and some of the men came to fell and remove the last sapling trunks. One day soon these would form part of the roof for our new village meeting house.

By late afternoon there was a large clear space and Abélé was keen to get busy with a hoe and turn the soil. I persuaded her that we had done enough for one day and that food should be our next priority. This time I would cook as I had managed to get some Indian spices in the town and had a fancy to make curry. We had bought meat in the market and already had rice and some vegetables in the house.

Abélé stayed close, helping chop and stir, watching everything I did as we chatted easily and the unusual aromas filled the air. From time to time someone would call out to ask what we were cooking or to comment on the appetising smell, but somehow they understood that we needed to be together and without company. Our meal was not quite ready when the early rain started so Abélé got two of the palm leaf capes and propped them up on long sticks over the cooking pots. I was a little worried that they might catch fire but she said the rain would keep the palm leaves damp enough to avoid burning, and they would not let water in to spoil the food. She was right and in the evening we enjoyed that food.

Later that evening I heard Mputu's voice in the village and called out for him to come over. We still had some curry left and Abélé proudly presented him with a bowl. I knew he would already have eaten, but he accepted it and tucked in. Moments later his eyes bulged and he gasped for water. I passed him the jug as Abélé started a fit of the giggles.

"What is this that put such fire in my belly?" he asked when he could speak again.

"Papa cooked it," Abélé told him. "You should eat more rice with it. Then it will not burn," she giggled impishly. "Anyway, you need to know what real fire in the belly is like. Papa needs you to mend the car and put fire in its belly so it will go. How can you do that if you do not know how the car must feel?"

All three of us fell to laughing over this piece of wisdom and I noticed that Mputu finished all the curry he had been given. I explained that Abélé's description of the Land Rover's needs was a little exaggerated and that really it was only the exhaust that was a problem. Mputu said he would fix it tomorrow and I asked him how he was getting on at the mill. He stayed with us for several hours before going back to his father's house and, although both were very discreet, I could not fail to notice the glances he and Abélé exchanged and the attention she gave him.

So, I thought, my speculations last night had been right after all. I felt pleased and was content to wait for events to come out right, as I thought they probably would. Not that I could afford to be complacent about that; I was still acutely aware of the menace posed by the man from Kimwamwa.

That night Abélé rolled her sleeping mat out inside in the corner of the house and I wondered if she too was having such thoughts and felt safer sleeping inside. Even so we both slept well, and the next day life seemed to have returned to normal.

I went off to the springs with the men and Abélé stayed in the village with the other women to weave new baskets and to braid fibre out of the vines cut from our banana patch. The men had worked well during my absence and progress had been good. The next filter box was nearly complete and they were beginning to fill the chambers with gravel, sand and charcoal. Within a few days we would be getting good clean water from this, the second spring.

We had talked about using large bamboo tubes to pipe the water closer to the village and some of the men went off in search of suitable materials. They were back within an hour, shouting and laughing, but without any bamboo. They had found a large thicket and had discovered an antelope trying to hide in it. The task in hand was instantly forgotten as they captured the beast and returned to the village, delighted with their trophy. This was typical of life here; a chaotic mixture of endeavour, opportunism and outrageous fun. The forest was generous and urgency was low, so what did it matter if it took another few days, or longer, to cut bamboo. Things that were needed got done eventually.

Work was abandoned for the day when the men returned to the village in a happy chattering, singing band. There would be plenty of meat for everyone and the rest of the day was spent roasting the carcass over a huge fire in the middle of the village and generally enjoying our joint good fortune. I noticed that some of the chattering biddies were not in evidence and mentioned it to Olidange.

"They will not dare come out after the telling off the Akuamba Kau gave them," he remarked with a grin.

"Even so," I said, "it would be unfair for them not to have some of the meat."

"You are too kind. They should have thought of such things

instead of trying to start trouble by their wicked talk. Your daughter is a good girl and should not be the victim of idle words from those who ought to know better. Let them do without," Olidange said and ambled off to talk to someone else.

Not long after that the meat was cooked and ready to be divided up. I noticed Abélé piling choice pieces into a basket. There was more than we required and I wondered why she was taking so much. It was unlike her to be greedy. As I watched, she took the basket and headed off towards the end of the village, away from our house. She entered one house and a few moments later came out, going on to another and then a third. I waited and watched.

After about ten minutes she came back, her basket empty, and returned to the fire for more meat. This time she only took a little and brought it over to share with me.

"That was a kind thing to do, Abélé," I told her as she sat down next to me. "Especially since their words could have caused trouble."

She smiled brightly, "They are old and few people pay any attention to them. Maybe they will think less badly of us for a small kindness."

"Maybe, but will they eat the meat you brought?"

"They are eating. I took the best cuts of the meat that only women may eat. They will know this and see it as a sign of respect. Wounds heal slowly in the forest, but faster when treated with the right medicine."

"You are wise beyond your years," I marvelled, realising how true that was.

"Akanku taught me that kindness costs little but can bring much."

"Then Akanku is also wise," I said, feeling very proud of them both.

For the next few days, life resumed its normal shape and I gave little thought to Kuloni Nkese. He had one week in which to return and accept the bride price and I doubted if he would come sooner. I reasoned that he would want to drag out my uncertainty until the very last moment, and by that time he could well have thought of a devious riposte that would wipe out any advantage I might have gained.

With no word from me, Abélé kept close to the village during that period. She spent most of her time either with a large band of children or, increasingly, with a group of young married women. She seemed happy enough, and was always smiling and laughing.

I went off into the forest each day with the village men and we worked on the springs. One of the young boys had drawn my attention to a soft, damp patch of ground on the slope not far above the village and we spent a morning clearing the undergrowth and digging about. It was a good find and with a little work we would have a new spring, much closer to the community, but Ekwona was keen to finish the other work before spending time on this one.

Work in the other villages was proceeding too, and I was due to make one of my regular circuits of visits within a few days. The day before I was to go, I asked Abélé if she would like to come too, for I would be away overnight. She thought about it for a moment and decided that she would prefer to stay in the village, unless I was going via the town. That was actually in the opposite direction, but I understood that she must be slightly reluctant to remain in the village without me there until the business with Kuloni Nkese was finally over, so I agreed and we set off early in the morning. I dropped her off with Akanku just as the sun rose over the steaming jungle.

There was a good road from the town that bypassed our part of the forest and would bring me within a few miles of my destination in a couple of hours. To call it a good road may be slightly misleading for in truth it was little more than a graded track through the smaller trees that littered the high ground above the gallery forest. In places it dived back into the deep forest to cross the river valleys. There it twisted and turned between the trees and the surface was rutted and, even on the upland stretches, cut by innumerable small streams and gullies where the heavy rain had eroded the exposed surface. For much of the way, one had to use four-wheel drive and it was impossible to go faster than thirty kilometres an hour at any point. It was, however, much faster going than by any of the forest roads and I arrived no later than if I had taken the more direct route from Inkwiti.

Progress on the work had also been good in this village and the men were proud of their achievements. They too had found new springs and wanted to develop them. It took quite a lot of discussion to persuade them that they should complete the work in hand before beginning any new sites, but eventually they saw the sense of this. We spent most of that day emptying and repacking one of the filter boxes where they had mistakenly put the charcoal and sand in the wrong chambers. With the error rectified we retired to their village for the night.

These folk, too, had heard about my encounter with Kuloni Nkese and wanted a first-hand account of the events. Strangely I had felt slightly apprehensive about discussing the matter in front of strangers, but their interest and evident support put me at ease and I found myself explaining once more how I had structured the bride price. It helped, in a way, to go through it all again, with independent people and away from the pressures of the moment.

Their approval for what I had decided was very reassuring. Here also Kuloni Nkese's reputation was well known and, although they had never had direct contact with the man, he was hated as if by proxy. They knew, of course, all about Abélé and how she had come to share my home. Word travelled fast and far in the forest, where everyone was hungry for news. They had never offered any opposition to our arrangement and would, I realised, be as averse as I was to that man succeeding in his cruel suit.

After a while, talk turned to more local matters and I heard amusing accounts of a recent hunting expedition made by the village boys. There were a group of youngsters in this village just approaching manhood who had decided to mount a hunt of their own to catch an *okapi*. While these animals were rare, and hunting them was forbidden by the government, they were occasionally seen in this part of the forest. Looking like something between a zebra and a giraffe, with a dark velvet body and striped hocks, the *okapi* was an animal of the deep jungle. Shy by nature, it avoided the areas most frequented by humans and was generally left unmolested since its strange appearance led the locals to believe that it was the embodiment of many of the benign spirits that guarded them in their forest home.

The village boys had heard that a lot of money could be gained by capturing an *okapi* alive. This, and the telling and retelling of the tale about the successful hunt, would contribute greatly to their status as they emerged into manhood, so they were determined to capture one. To plan such a hunt and to fail would reduce their worth in the eyes of their elders, so the preparation was all done in secret. Out in the forest, they cut vines and wove nets and ropes. Strong poles were prepared from which a cage could be rapidly constructed once an animal had been caught, and these were hidden just outside their village. Eventually everything was ready and the boys set out.

For two days, they scoured the area where the last sighting had been made, but without success. One or two of the younger boys became bored and turned their attention to other things like catching the enormous, brilliantly coloured butterflies that fluttered about in the forest canopy and among the heavily scented flowers that bloomed in the top layers of the dense undergrowth.

Crawling out along a slender branch, twenty feet above the ground, one of the smaller boys had his attention fixed on a large, iridescent blue butterfly that was gently fanning its wings dry where it had just emerged from the chrysalis. As he reached out to capture his prey, the branch snapped and he fell into a dense tangle of undergrowth. His descent was applauded by hoots of laughter from his friends. On the way down his head connected with something hard and he lay stunned for a few moments.

Regaining his senses he felt something soft brushing against his leg and opened his eyes to find a young *okapi* bending over him, its large, liquid brown eyes watching with curiosity and its muzzle brushing gently against his skin as it sniffed his scent.

Too surprised to shout, the boy lay there and gazed back with amazement. When his friends called out asking him if he was all right he told them quietly that the animal was there. Their attention returned immediately to the original purpose of their expedition. As fast and quietly as possible, they spread out their nets and surrounded the tangled patch. The animal lifted its head, perfectly aware of their presence, but made no move to flee. Within a few minutes the capture was complete and the smallest boy in the band was a hero.

With efficient despatch and treating the young *okapi* remarkably gently, the boys had carried their prize home. A stockade was soon erected in their village and the *okapi* was penned, becoming immediately the focus of everyone's attention.

That evening the boys told their tale and received the praise of the other villagers. But one old man asked why the final capture had been so easy, almost as if the *okapi* had wanted to be taken. This raised other speculations. People began to wonder about the wisdom of selling the animal and risking the wrath of the spirits. That it had been hunted and caught was enough, it was argued. Since the villagers seldom used money, the young men's status could be more enhanced by returning the host of their guardian spirits to freedom in the forest than by sending the animal into eternal captivity away from its forest home.

At dawn, the boy who had fallen at the animal's feet went quietly and opened the stockade. The young *okapi* ambled out and melted into the forest. When the other villagers woke, they found the boy sitting beside the empty stockade and realised what he had done. He received clucks of approval from the adults and no reproof from the other boys in the hunting band.

A few days later the Akuamba Kau arrived and conducted the ceremony that initiated the boys into manhood. While nobody had mentioned the incident, none was surprised that he already knew and approved of the young man's decision to release his captive. The spirits would look favourably on the village, he said, for they had treated the spirits' host with kindness.

NEXT MORNING I SET OFF EARLY, with a slightly fuzzy head from drinking too much palm wine the night before. Taking the tortuous forest road, I arrived back in the village before midday to find the place buzzing with activity and excitement.

Hearing my vehicle arrive, Ekwona came over and I could see from his face that something dire had happened. I imagined all sorts of horrors as I climbed from the driving seat. My immediate fear was that something had happened to Abélé.

"What is it, Ekwona? That man has not come here again, has he?" I asked.

"No. He has not been here," the headman told me, sitting down on one of the logs in front of my house. "Even so, he has made trouble. We have heard that he took a woman in Kimwamwa. He used her and then killed her. You should go now and find Nkwanu Knaii. This will be his business."

There were a hundred questions I wanted to ask, but Ekwona's manner told me that he knew little more. The best thing would be to let Nkwanu Knaii know as soon as possible and leave him to deal with it. I had promised, in any case, to go back today and collect Abélé and I needed to take all my fuel cans to the town and fill them with petrol.

Ekwona helped me strap the jerry cans into their racks in the back of the Land Rover and I set off, taking with me a couple of villagers who wanted to visit the market. They had heard the news and were speculating wildly as I drove out of the village on the track up to the main road. The rain had eaten away more soil around the tree that marked the junction, and I had to shunt back and forth to get round. This stopped the speculation as we were tossed about in the jolting cab, and we agreed that someone would have to come and repair the track before the rain made it completely impassable; if not, the tree could soon topple and block the road completely.

A kilometre or so after joining the road, we rounded a bend and came face to face with a large truck coming in the other direction. It was heavily loaded, as trucks in this part of the world invariably are. It was also coming downhill, and completely filled the narrow road. The truck could not go backwards, so there was nothing for it but for me to reverse, then pull off the road and let it pass. This was not a simple as it may sound. The undergrowth on either side was dense and had to be cut back to enable me to get off the track.

My friends leaped out with the machetes that always lived in the Land Rover for this purpose, and started hacking. After a few moments they realised that this part of the road was closely flanked by heavy tree trunks and they moved back down the hill to look for a space. I went to talk to the truck driver and enquire where he was going. He turned out to be a friendly fellow whom I had met several times before, so we spent a few moments exchanging news before I too went to help carve out a passing place.

It took at least half an hour to clear an adequate lay-by, and another ten minutes to reverse the Land Rover safely downhill to it.

Eventually the truck went past and we got back on the road, arriving in the town with no further delays. I went directly to the filling station but was told there was no fuel and I would have to wait at least a week before any more arrived. This was not an uncommon occurrence and just another of the inconveniences one learned to live with in this country.

My friends had left me and gone off to the market, so with only mild disappointment, I drove round to the Party office in search of Nkwanu Knaii. He was again doing battle with the inadequate telephone system trying, with only marginal success, to confer with a colleague in the regional headquarters. As before, he waved me to the bench under the window and one of his aides appeared with a glass of sticky tea. He must have read the anxiety on my face for he abruptly ended his call and asked me what was wrong.

I explained what Ekwona had said and told him the rumours

and speculation that were flying about. He asked a few questions, but I had no answers. Decisively he said, "This is Party business, so I will have to go there, but my Toyota is broken. Will you take me, Kamran?"

"I would, but I have almost no fuel. I have just come from the filling station and they tell me that they have none left and I will have to wait a week for the next delivery."

Nkwanu Knaii took a piece of official paper from his desk drawer and wrote hastily. "They keep a reserve for official use. Take this and tell them to fill your tank and every spare can you have. You will be taking me on official business so the Party will pay for this. One of my assistants will go with you." He passed me the note, called the assistant who had brought my tea and gave rapid instructions.

We went back to the petrol station where, miraculously, there was now plenty of fuel and the grinning attendant filled all my tanks and jerry cans. The assistant signed some forms and we went back to the office where Nkwanu Knaii was waiting on the doorstep giving instructions to another assistant.

We called briefly at his house to let Akanku and Abélé know where we were going, then took the road to Kimwamwa. Like the road to Inkwiti, this was mainly through the forest and very slow going, twisting between huge trees, across innumerable small streams and rivers, up and down steep valley sides. As the crow flies Kimwamwa was only about sixty kilometres away, but on that winding route it was nearer eighty-five. We met five or six vehicles coming the other way, with all the usual delays such encounters entailed, reversing and hacking out passing places each time. At one point we came up behind a huge wagon that had broken down, completely blocking the road.

Nkwanu Knaii got out to see what the trouble was and found that the old Berliet had lost a front wheel and would not be moving from there for a long time. There was nothing for it but to turn round and go back to where the last track joined the road and then try to work our way round. The side track seemed quite passable at first but soon degenerated to a tangled tunnel, overgrown with creepers and fallen branches, barely even passable on foot.

We stopped the vehicle and waded forward on foot for some distance to reconnoitre ahead. After a short distance the passage appeared to improve and we decided to cut our way through rather than backtrack again and risk losing many more hours. Laboriously we hacked and slashed at the undergrowth until our arms and wrists were numb and bruised. We were soon covered in scratches and minor cuts and our sweating bodies had attracted an unwelcome host of insects. By the time dusk came, we were almost through. I went back to bring the Land Rover forward while Nkwanu cut down the last few feet of the obstruction.

I thought we must have stopped with one wheel in a hole for the Land Rover was leaning heavily to the left. Walking round to look at it, I found that the back tyre was flat, ripped open by sharp stone or a hard root. The ground here was soggy and not really suitable for jacking up a vehicle with no solid base under the jack. I had a small board in the back for just this purpose, but it was not enough and just sank into the mud as soon as I cranked the jack handle.

Again we hacked at the jungle and collected enough sticks to make a thick mat. With the board on top of this we eventually managed to crank the jack up far enough to change the wheel. It took a further two hours before we were moving again. By that time the evening rain had begun and our progress was painfully slow. I remarked on this and asked my friend if he thought the forest was trying to tell us something and perhaps we were not supposed to arrive too soon.

"You are becoming as superstitious as these forest villagers," he laughed. "Perhaps you have been here too long." He paused as the vehicle bucked hard over an exposed root and he had to hang on to avoid being thrown about the cab. "But maybe you are right," he resumed at last, "it is certainly not an easy journey and we are only halfway there."

SOON AFTER THAT WE CAME TO the first of four river crossings. This part of the country has many small rivers, all about six feet deep and fifty or so yards wide, fast flowing and clear. At these crossings there were ferries, most installed many years ago in the colonial era, consisting of a flat-bottomed barge linked with pulleys to a stout cable across the river. By angling the barge across the current, the flow was used to propel it from one bank to the other. Almost inevitably the ferry had just reached the far bank when we arrived. There was a lorry waiting ahead of us and the ferry could only take one vehicle at a time.

I suppose Nkwanu Knaii could have used his position as Party agent to get us across before the lorry but he seemed reluctant to use his authority on this occasion. This looked like being an all-night journey anyway, so we settled down to wait our turn.

Some enterprising person had set up stall next to the crossing, selling food. The appetising aroma soon attracted us and we sat under a small thatched shelter to eat roasted taro yams with a thick sauce of fish and forest leaves. Half a packet of cigarettes was enough to trade for a bunch of bananas.

We had finished our meal long before it was our turn to cross the river. Eventually our turn came and we struggled through slippery mud up the far bank and plunged again into the dark tunnel of the forest road.

There were three more rivers and each time we had to wait. It was light long before we crossed the final one and again we stopped by the side of the road to eat, asking how far it was to Kimwamwa. About three hours' walk, the food seller told us, but there was trouble there and we would be advised to stay away.

We asked her what sort of trouble, but she did not know any details, just that it was bad trouble and that the feared and terrible Party agent was involved. She advised us to take the next fork and bypass Kimwamwa, almost as if the place had an evil spell cast on it. The woman obviously did not know who my companion was, since he wore no uniform or badge of office and she made no enquiry about why we should want to go there.

We paid for our food and left, wondering just what trouble was waiting for us. I noticed that Nkwanu Knaii had tossed a heavy bag into the back of the vehicle before we left his office and I had heard a distinct metallic clank as it landed. Perhaps he was going to arrest Kuloni Nkese and had brought along some manacles. Even if only a fraction of the stories I had heard were true, it was high time that man was locked away.

The road struggled on and became more difficult. This part of the forest seemed to be even thicker than the area I was familiar with, and the road was more overgrown. When I remarked on this Nkwanu told me it was no thicker, it was just that the road was little used and therefore not kept as well cleared as nearer home. Why not, I enquired, since Kimwamwa must be considerably bigger than our village. He smiled and asked if I would run wagons through such a place with that man there to extort tolls and rob my cargoes. As it was, he had heard stories of villagers going elsewhere to buy goods only to have them pillaged when they returned home. I asked why nothing had ever been done about it and he told me that there was no hard evidence and without a formal complaint, the Party authorities would not bother to investigate too closely. As a result, prosperity in this area had evaporated. The people were cowed into submissive silence.

"They should incorporate this area into your sector," I said, considering what he had told me.

"Don't think I haven't suggested it, but until he is moved, or does something criminal that can be proved, there is nothing to be done," my friend said. "They are good people here and deserve better."

Just then we came up a long slope and the forest thinned as we reached a village. "This is Kimwamwa," Nkwanu Knaii said, looking ahead to where a large crowd was milling about.

Chapter 12

I PARKED UNDER A TALL TEAK tree at the beginning of the village and we climbed out, stiff and weary after almost twenty hours of arduous travel. There seemed to be a party in progress in the centre of the village. Smoke and flames were rising from a fire which was surrounded by a crowd of villagers. People were singing and dancing and the air resonated to the frenetic beat of heavy drums. While the forest people were always energetic in their festivities, this had a subtly different quality about it. It made Nkwanu and I look at one another with the same questioning lift of eyebrows.

"What's going on?" I wondered aloud.

"I think we are about to find out," Nkwanu said, indicating a scrawny man who had detached himself from the milling mob and was weaving an unsteady path towards us. "It undoubtedly has something to do with Kuloni Nkese and probably also that thing on the pole over there beyond the crowd. Maybe this time he has gone too far."

The lurching man was nearer now and others, noticing our arrival, were approaching in small groups. The man stopped in front of us carrying a piece of charred meat on a stick.

"Welcome," he said with a decidedly drunken slur in his voice. He shuffled his feet to maintain his balance as he made an expansive gesture with the piece of meat.

"Are you having a party?" I enquired.

"No, we are having the Party man!" he said and dissolved into a fit of laughter. "Join us and have some," he suggested, offering me the piece of meat.

"What is that?" I asked.

"The Party man," he said, laughing again. "We are eating him. Have some."

Suddenly it all became clear. I looked again at the object high on the pole beyond the revellers. Shrouded by a cloud of insects, it was undoubtedly a human head; one, moreover, that I had been dreading seeing again. I had not expected to encounter it like this.

The man offered the meat again. "Have some meat."

"No thank you," I said, trying to suppress my revulsion, "I never liked the man when he was alive, I doubt if cooking will have improved him. What has happened? Why have you done this thing?"

Others had crowded round and began ushering us forward to the centre of all the activity. As we drew close to the fire I looked again at the top of the pole. It was indeed Kuloni Nkese's head, battered and hacked from his body, impaled on a long sharpened sapling to oversee his own funeral feast. His face, never handsome, bore numerous new scars and was contorted in a savage, snarling rictus, the eyes bulging and staring blindly through surrounding cloud of furiously buzzing flies.

I turned to Nkwanu Knaii and found him deep in conversation with a dignified little man who was talking very fast and quietly, obviously explaining what had happened. I moved closer to listen but the man lowered his voice and I was unable to catch his words.

My attention was claimed by a woman who thrust a roasted taro yam into my hand and another who offered a gourd of something that smelled alcoholic.

Not quite sure how to react, I indicated that she should offer it first to Nkwanu Knaii. I would see what he did and follow his lead. With a brief nod of thanks he accepted the gourd and drank. When he passed it to me, I drank too and passed it on to someone else. I accepted the yam and, as I bit into it, realised that I was very hungry. The smell of roasting meat made me wonder if there was anything more conventional being cooked for – and it shames me to admit it – Kuloni Nkese actually smelled quite appetising. I decided it would be better not to ask and took another bite of the yam.

Cannibalism was supposed to have died out in Africa seventy or eighty years ago, although I had come across three incidents in Ghana, Eastern Nigeria and Cameroon some years previously. As had been the case on those occasions, in the few instances when it was practised, cannibalism was a minor, but significant, part of other most secret and sacred rituals. It usually involved infants or the deformed children who were considered to be the embodiment of evil spirits, rather than adults in the full vigour of life. Even in the days when it was more common, it had been confined to ritual and symbolic events and was not simply some hungry fellow looking for a tasty meal as some of the more romantic writers of the nineteenth century suggested. Sometimes it had been to confirm dominance of the spirit over an enemy defeated in battle, sometimes to absorb the victim's spiritual power, and sometimes to unite spirits in a perpetual bond that cemented family or tribal alliances. The reasons were many and always loaded with ritual significance.

So it was in this instance. Although I knew there had been trouble here in Kimwamwa, this was not what I had expected to discover, yet I cannot say I was shocked by what these people were doing. When I thought about it later, it all made perfect sense to me; the tyrant had overstepped the line of tolerance and his subjects had toppled him. Revenge had been taken and his spirit was consigned to ignominious oblivion without taking its place among the ancestors. By ending it this way his spirit would not be free to roam the forest, to haunt the village and continue the torment he had practised while alive. Justice had been done.

After a few more minutes, Nkwanu Knaii touched my arm and indicated that we should go to the village meeting house. He had asked the village elders to meet us there and give a full account of what had happened. He had been recognised by the little man, who turned out to be the headman, and a number of others who, far from being wary of his presence as I half expected, seemed to welcome him. He was evidently known and respected beyond his borders. The people treated him with open respect but as an equal. They appeared to have no fear of the Party despite the fact that one of its officials had been brutally slaughtered and made the central ingredient of a public barbecue. Surely there would be some reckoning for this, even if the victim had been an inhuman monster. In any case, I had always been told that since cannibalism had officially died out, it was now a capital offence.

As we waited on grass mats under the huge thatched roof of their meeting place, the village elders assembled and sat in a semicircle facing us. Gourds of the fermented brew were brought and I wondered how much had already been consumed. Surprisingly, none of the people there appeared to be the worse for it, however much they had drunk, and their speech was clear and lucid. They were all, however, in a state of highly charged excitement.

Slowly the sorry tale unravelled under Nkwanu Knaii's patient questioning. The people of Kimwamwa all knew about me and my work with the other villages, and it had even been suggested once that I should be contacted and my help requested. In the end nothing had been done because Kuloni Nkese had heard of the idea and forbidden it, saying he would not permit any interfering *mundele* to meddle in his sector.

Kimwamwa had, of course, heard all about his intention of taking Abélé as his bride. Kuloni Nkese had bragged about it when news first reached him that she had come to live in my house. This didn't surprise me since, in the forest, everyone knows everything of interest about everyone else's business, even people who live many days walk away. Being an outsider and white, I and my activities might expect to attract more than passing attention. Anyway, Kuloni Nkese had frequently boasted about how he would have me on my knees at his feet, begging him to take the girl as his bride; about how he would publicly humiliate me by deflowering her in front of me and all my friends in the village. I began to realise there were ramifications to this affair I had never even dreamed of, and a cold shiver went down my spine.

They had known the day before he came to demand that I set the bride price, because the Party agent had got roaring drunk on palm wine, then made them listen to his flights of fancy and lurid descriptions of how he would ensnare me by invoking the local customs. They told me later that his knowledge of local custom was very limited and highly coloured by his own concept of what common practice ought to be. My own understanding, on the other hand, seemed to merit some measure of genuine respect. They all knew I had been initiated with the *ebugo* root ceremony before Abélé had come to live in my house.

Kuloni Nkese had told them that nothing could save me from his plan. "Even the President, who is his friend of many years, cannot help him," he told them. "Once I have taken the one he calls his daughter, I shall have him as my slave." This came as another surprise to me. While I knew he was aware that I had met the President – he had told me this himself – I had never imagined that he knew more; few people did, for I had not advertised the fact that I had known Mobutu for many years and considered him a friend.

He boasted that he knew, even before he asked it, what bride price I would ask. I would not ask for goods or money, he had said, because I lived like a pauper. I would ask for something stupid like a village school, he had forecast. Whatever it was would have no meaning. It would leave me with nothing but my stupid white principles, and he spat on the floor saying, "I will chew and spit him out like this, and grind him under my heel," and he had stamped the spittle into the dirt.

This was another shock and I realised how badly I had underestimated the man. I had been totally out of my depth and sublimely ignorant of the fact. Even the feedback I had received from my friends in the village had given me little inkling of this, so maybe they too had been deluded. I felt an upwelling of relief that the man was now dead. It was squashed almost at once by the realisation that having misjudged him so badly before, I could easily be doing so again. He might be dead, but what hidden traps had he laid for me before his demise? My moment of euphoria turned instantly to sour gloom. Would I ever be free of this man?

After all his boasting, Kuloni Nkese had grabbed two of the village men and literally frog-marched them out of the village to accompany him to Inkwiti and serve as his witnesses for the naming of the bride price. I had met these men and saw them now sitting in the rows of people before us. I nodded to both of them as our eyes met and was answered by both with a smile and a friendly nod.

Everyone in Kimwamwa obviously knew all the details of the bride price for the two men had come straight home as fast as they could after Kuloni Nkese had stormed off in a rage. I got the impression they had enjoyed their moment of glory, being present at the humiliation of their hated master and then being home first to tell the tale, no doubt suitably embellished.

It had taken the two men all night and most of the next morning to get home on foot, but they had still arrived two full days before Kuloni Nkese. He swept into the village in his official Toyota, having come by a different route than the one we had been forced to take. He drove straight over a basket of fowl, dropped by a frightened woman as he steered straight at her, blasted the horn and made her leap aside in alarm. When she saw what he had done to her fowl, she screamed and yelled at him, demanding that he pay for the fowls. In response, he had grabbed her by the hair and started hauling her towards his own house.

There were few people around in the village at the time and the sound of the big man shouting at someone was generally a signal to keep out of sight and mind one's own business, so none of the adults actually saw any of this. The woman's two children were the only direct witnesses and ran after them shouting for him to let their mother alone. In response, he kicked the daughter so hard that she flew against a nearby tree and suffered a broken arm. Before he could escape, her younger brother, who must have been about nine years old, had been seized roughly by the leg, swung round Kuloni Nkese's head and launched into a thicket. It was probably his good fortune that he landed in a tangle of undergrowth where the forest was encroaching between the houses for it softened his landing and saved him from serious injury.

Fuelled with alcohol and anger over the bride price, Kuloni Nkese dragged the woman into his house, ripped the clothes from her body and savagely raped her. He must have used her several times before he broke her neck, for the children could hear her screams.

Other villagers, who came some time later to help the little girl and to pull her brother from the tangled vines, said they also had heard her cries. None had dared approach the house for fear of the big man's anger, but when the woman's husband returned from the forest and heard what was happening, he acted at once.

Without a moment's hesitation he picked up a flat stone, took out his machete and began to sharpen it as he strode towards the big man's house. He was almost there when Kuloni Nkese emerged, eyes staring and crazed, with fresh blood on his hands. The man screamed and leaped forward to attack. His machete buried itself in the big man's arm and was wrenched from his grasp as Kuloni Nkese swung away from him. With a roaring bellow the big man leaped on the unfortunate husband and battered him to the ground. Leaving the husband stunned and dizzy, Kuloni Nkese then fled between the houses and vanished into the forest.

That had been five days ago, they told us.

By the time the husband had recovered his senses, a crowd had gathered and someone peeped warily round the door of Kuloni Nkese's house. The woman's lifeless, naked body was sprawled on the floor. Emotions that were already running high ignited into vengeful fury. Leaving their women to care for and console the injured children and to deal with the woman's body, the men ran for their hunting weapons. Within half an hour, every able-bodied man in Kimwamwa had entered the forest, following the trail of blood from the big man's injured arm until it became too dark to see the splashes clearly. The best hunting trackers in the village took charge and led their brothers onwards.

At first their pursuit was accompanied by a great deal of noise which can only have served to warn their quarry and tell him which way to move for safety. After a while a few men broke away from the main band and moved silently off towards each flank. They were followed soon after by other silent groups while the remaining group spread out slightly and continued to move forward, making as much noise as possible. The tactic was designed to make their quarry move out to the flanks and then to catch him unawares, but they underestimated the big man. He may have been terribly drunk but evidently the events of the last few hours had sobered him. He had also lived in Kimwamwa long enough to have learned something of the hunting techniques employed by these people. For a big man he was able to move remarkably easily in the dense jungle, and it was entirely possible that he had been passed in a dense thicket some way back towards the village.

The hunt slowed down but continued nonetheless all through the night. By dawn everyone was silent but the rage that drove them gave the men energy and kept tiredness at bay. Some picked leaves from bushes as they passed and chewed them for the stimulants they contained, but most just concentrated on watching the jungle and keeping their place in the hunting line.

It took three and a half days for the men of Kimwamwa to catch up with Kuloni Nkese. During this time, they neither slept nor paused for food. As they crossed streams they would kneel briefly and drink; as they passed fruit trees they picked ripe fruits and ate them on the march. Most of the time they moved forward in line with single-minded purpose, alert to the sounds and signs of the forest, experienced hunters all, intent on one quarry alone among the dozens that appeared before them.

When he was finally caught, Kuloni Nkese was trying to climb the tangled roots of a fig tree at the base of a small cliff. He was exhausted and covered in lacerations with his clothes in tatters. There was no whoop of triumph when he was sighted, just a cold purposeful advance and a smart crack on the head with a hunting club. That was enough to knock him senseless, but no more.

The men of Kimwamwa trussed Kuloni Nkese like a pig. Binding him to a stout pole, they suspended it between two trees, well above the ground. Then they settled down to rest. Some went off into the forest and came back with enough meat to feed everyone a light meal. A few collected fruit, some made a fire and others brought water from the stream a few yards back from the cliff. After eating the whole party settled down to sleep.

Kuloni Nkese regained his senses before dawn and started to bellow and rant. Deciding that since the words he used were so foul he must enjoy filth in his mouth, one on the hunters walked a few yards into the forest and returned with a handful of maggoty dung left by a forest elephant. He crammed this into the yelling man's mouth and bound a cloth over the top to keep it in place. That brought silence and the approval of everyone in the hunting party.

When morning came the men brought their captive down from the trees and hoisted him onto their shoulders, still bound to the pole, and started homewards. It was a long journey, hacking their way through the undergrowth and occasionally following established game trails for a few yards. When night came they made camp again and once more hoisted their captive up clear of the ground. At dawn they set off on the last few miles and arrived home within an hour or so.

Several men had gone ahead the previous night to spread the news. With one accord the villagers gathered wood and built a huge pyre in the centre of the village. When the hunters arrived all was ready. The headman came forward as they lowered Kuloni Nkese to the ground and removed the cloth that bound his mouth. Parched though he must have been, the big brute managed to spit out the remaining dung and began at once to curse and shout. The villagers stood and looked on for a few moments, then the headman ordered the fire to be lit. He handed his machete to the husband of the woman Kuloni Nkese had used so cruelly and stepped back.

The man walked slowly forward, drew his knife and cut the cords that bound the big man to his pole. After so long trussed tightly, and weakened by the hunt, the big man could not move. The bereaved husband bent down and ripped open the front of his trousers, took hold and with a quick flick of his knife he cut off Kuloni Nkese's genitals. This brought a bellow of agony from the big man, but still he could not move. The husband stuffed the severed parts into the big man's open mouth, pushing them further in with the handle of his machete. Kuloni Nkese's face contorted with renewed hatred as the man stood and raised his machete.

The severed head was impaled on the sharpened end of a sapling which was then stuck in the ground with its grisly burden high above the pyre. Then Kuloni Nkese's body was stripped and thrown onto the fire. The drummers started pounding out a frenetic rhythm. Gourds of palm wine and other fermented brews were passed round as the villagers began an ancient and only dimly remembered ritual dance around the fire. The stench of burning flesh added to the passion of the event and turned the dancing into a frenzy. As the fire reduced to glowing logs, people stepped forward and carved hunks of meat from the body, stuffing them into their mouths as they returned to the dance.

Less than an hour after this started, Nkwanu Knaii and I had arrived in the village.

The dancing had continued throughout the telling of this sorry tale. By the time the telling was complete, there was nothing left of Kuloni Nkese but a pile of ash and his head on the pole. Nkwanu Knaii told the headman to have it removed, taken into the forest and buried in an ant heap. The headman gave his orders and the two men who had witnessed the bride price went off to deal with it.

Nkwanu Knaii turned to me and asked, "Did you understand all that?"

"Unfortunately, yes," I answered. "What happens now? He was a cruel man and had done many wrong things, but to be killed like that..."

"Under normal circumstances these villagers would have to face the law like everywhere else," he interrupted me. "But there is no police post within fifty kilometres of Kimwamwa and, even if the police investigated, it is unlikely they would ever uncover the truth. I think we know more of that than anyone. As the senior government official on the scene, it falls to me to decide. Since he was a Party agent, the Party would have to be involved anyway. It is better that we finish this thing today and let it rest. The people can get on with their lives, which have already had too much disruption. There is nothing to be gained from inflicting more suffering."

"But what about the cannibalism? Surely you cannot approve?" I asked.

"Approval does not come into it. In the normal course of events cannibalism is against the law, yes, and the penalties are very severe. But this is no ordinary case. This was a man who took every opportunity for cruelty; who abused his power so much that deep feelings have been awakened. What he did was not only criminal, it was also an affront to the spiritual foundations and integrity of these people. On top of everything else he had done, to assault children begging for mercy on behalf of their mother, to rape and murder the mother and then to run away and hide was a most wicked thing that demands communal retribution. The spirits were roused to anger and drove their people to this. The only way to appease them was to hunt and kill the culprit and then to eat him, leaving his rotten soul to burn in the fire so that his spirit is destroyed. It must be so or else he would come back as an evil *dishi* to attack them. By ancient custom what these simple people have done was not wrong. They would never normally do something like this. These are good people, like all your friends in Inkwiti. How can I judge them and punish something that was outside their control?"

He looked round the faces of the villagers seated in front of us and I looked also. As he had said, they were just like my friends back in Inkwiti, full of the same vitality and fun, subject to the same taboos, the same fears and doubts; people making the best they could of a difficult environment, living in harmony with it and subject to all its influences. Into their lives had come a monster with the authority of the government behind him. They had been forced to bend to his will, to do and to tolerate many things that were contrary to their customs and their moral values.

Under extreme provocation they had finally turned on the tyrant, becoming the agents of his downfall. Now they were free again to lead their lives as they and their ancestors for generations before them had always done. I looked round the faces and saw no downcast eyes, no frowns of doubt, no head turned away in shame. They had done only what they had to do and saw no wrong in it. Nor should they, I realised, for to be ashamed now would be to abrogate the principles by which they lived.

By now it was late afternoon and to start home would mean doing most of the journey by night a second time. Everyone was tired and in need of sleep. The women brought yams and manioc porridge with small grilled fish on sticks. There was no meat, and Nkwanu Knaii told me later that they would not eat meat again in Kimwamwa until the moon had changed three times. Although her body had been consigned to the forest, they still had the mourning ritual to perform for the murdered woman. Her spirit must be honoured and given to the ancestors.

Chapter 13

WE ATE AND THEN SLEPT. IN the morning, Nkwanu Knaii had another talk with the headman before we left to take the tortuous road home. The women gave us a basket of fruit and the two men who had sat in witness of her bride price gave me two beautifully cured antelope hides as a gift for my daughter.

Once more on the road, we talked little at first. I began to wonder what part my bride price had played in Kuloni Nkese's terrible behaviour. Had I so enraged him that he got drunk and did these dreadful things as an act of revenge? Then why had he not come and taken out his rage on me? I wondered how Abélé would react when she was told, then remembered the way she had so casually dismissed the matter before when I had explained how I had structured the bride price and had told her that I would never allow the big man to have her. Maybe she could simply shut this out too. Would this, I wondered, have repercussions in years to come?

After a while I told Nkwanu Knaii of my thoughts and we talked them through. He agreed that perhaps Kuloni Nkese had been angered when he understood the true nature of the bride price, but by that time he had probably already consumed a lot of drink.

Maybe he still had intentions of entangling me in some devious plot that we still knew nothing about. In any event, Nkwanu reasoned, he probably seized the woman in Kimwamwa on a drunken impulse because she had rebuked him over her basket of fowl. He had lashed out at the children because they were interfering. He may not have intended to kill the woman, merely to use her, but by struggling and fighting back, she had made him use more force. In his drunken state, he had less control and overdid it, so he broke her neck.

"You sound as if you're defending him!" I said in amazement.

"Never! There is no defence. I'm merely trying to explain the probable course of events, to let you see that you cannot hold yourself responsible. If you had named a simple bride price of goods and money, he would have taken this as a victory and got drunk to celebrate. All the events that followed could just as easily have been the same. It was the evil in him that caused these things. You are not to blame."

"Even so, it makes me wonder."

"Wonder all you like, my friend, but understand this: what I have just said is the official version. That is what will be recorded. Whatever doubts you have, keep them to yourself. It will do others no good for you to have thoughts like that." His tone made it very clear that the matter was now closed and not open to further discussion.

I knew that what he had said was true. There are times when it is wiser just to accept. I must turn my attention to the future and put this terrible business where it belonged, firmly in the past.

The road was hardly any easier in daylight than it had been the previous night. We were, however, more fortunate with the ferries and found each one on our side of its river with nothing waiting to

The Land Rover emerging from dense forest.

cross. This saved us several hours and we reached Inkwiti in the late afternoon.

Hearing the Land Rover, Ekwona emerged from his hut and came to talk to us. A few minutes later, the Akuamba Kau materialised out of the forest and we were joined by one or two other men. Nkwanu Knaii explained that we were on our way back from Kimwamwa to Kikwit and had only stopped off to let people know what was going on. He told them the official version of events, but gave little detail and said that the matter was now finished. As far as the village people were concerned, Kuloni Nkese had died as a result of his own actions and accordingly his suit for Abélé was ended. We should now forget him and get on with our lives.

We sat in Ekwona's house and talked through the worst of the early evening rain then, as it eased off, we climbed wearily into the vehicle again and headed back to the town. I had driven most of the way from Kimwamwa and gladly accepted when Nkwanu offered to take the wheel. Tired though I was, there was no possibility of sleep as he drove, for the rough road had us leaning first one way and then the other and I had to hold on tight or be tossed from my seat. We talked little now. Eventually, after what seemed like half the night, the first lights of the town came in sight as we emerged from the dense forest on the long slope up to the plateau.

We went first to the Party office so that Nkwanu could contact his boss, but the phone lines were down and he could not get through. He left instructions with the duty assistant to call him immediately it was working again and we went across town to his house. Watching the people that we passed in the streets, going about their routine business, I was struck by how normal everything seemed here. The nightmare at Kimwamwa took a step back.

Abélé was waiting at the compound gate as we pulled up. She had been listening for the Land Rover and, despite the late hour, was alert and eager to see us. Akanku told me later that she had been hovering all day, waiting for our return, with food ready for us. Although Nkwanu and I would both have preferred simply to tell them the bare bones of the news and drop onto our sleeping mats, they would have none of it, but Akanku insisted that we eat properly first.

We did as we were told and after the meal Nkwanu told them that the Party agent from Kimwamwa was dead and that Abélé need have no more fear of him. The matter was now one for the Party to sort out and he would be in contact with his superiors the next day. We should try to forget it all and get on with out lives.

Akanku obviously wanted to hear all the details, but I was not surprised when Abélé simply said it was good that the matter was ended like this for now it could never come back to haunt us. She asked no questions and seemed relaxed and happy to have us both back. I suspected she would ask me the details when we got home but, for the time being at least, she was satisfied.

The night was hot and humid and I elected to sleep under the thatched shelter in the courtyard where I could benefit from any small movement in the air. As I lay down on my mat, Abélé rolled over in her corner and I could see the starlight reflecting in her eyes. "Thank you for making me safe, Papa. You can sleep peacefully now," she whispered, and it was the last thing I remembered until morning. Remembering this on waking, I wondered for a moment if Abélé thought I had killed her monster and decided that she would have to know the truth.

After extracting promises from our friends to visit us very soon in Inkwiti, Abélé and I made a brief visit to the market before going home. The sun was bright and the colours of the landscape on the open plateau were vivid and very beautiful. Through the first part of the forest, as we descended into the valley, dappled sunlight cast golden highlights on the road and we saw the brilliant flash of gaudy birds and flickering butterflies. It was as if the world had renewed itself after the drama of the last few days. I felt invigorated and happy; Abélé was in a sparkling mood too and chatted easily about all sorts of everyday things.

Inevitably the villagers would want to talk about the events we had witnessed in Kimwamwa, but they need no longer feel threatened by Kuloni Nkese or his memory. For me too it would be necessary to talk it all through again before the ghost could be settled and life could go forward, but we had plenty of time for that.

Chapter 14

A PILE OF FRESH FRUIT, COLLECTED that morning by our neighbours, was heaped outside our door and some kind soul had replenished the *akwali* pots with fresh clean water. Olidange told us later that this was the first drawing of water from the newly completed filter on our second spring. I felt honoured that they had given this to me. People called out in greeting as we arrived and one or two paused briefly to chat about the inconsequential things of everyday life.

People drifted back early from their daily tasks and in the afternoon I went and sat with Ekwona on the rock outside his house. People gathered and sat on the ground around us chatting quietly amongst themselves, waiting. I knew the Akuamba Kau would come, even though no one had mentioned him, and was not surprised to see him stalk quietly out of the forest and sit on a log just behind the crowd of expectant villagers.

Looking around their faces I saw all my friends, but realised also that some people were missing. "The old women are not here," I remarked to Ekwona.

"They are still in their houses, according to the Wise One's order," he responded. "They will not dare come out until he permits."

"Would it not be better for them to hear this now?" I asked, and was about to make the request when I noticed Abélé approach the witch doctor and speak to him. He listened quietly, thought for a moment, then got up and went to summon the old women.

They came in a gaggle, silent, subdued and shuffling, their heads bowed low to sit in a stiff row off to one side; outside the main gathering but well within earshot. The Akuamba Kau resumed his seat and nodded to me to begin. As I marshalled my thoughts, Abélé came and sat on the ground by my feet, leaning back against my shins as they dangled over the edge of the rock.

The words came and I told the story with all my thoughts and fears. I left out none of the gruesome detail for the villagers were as involved as I was and had the right to know. I told them what the people of Kimwamwa had told us, and what Nkwanu Knaii had done and said. I told them that there would be no investigation by the police because Nkwanu Knaii had been there and would deal with the matter officially. I told them that Kuloni Nkese's suit for my daughter had really been an attack on me and I explained that the whole business had been the product of his experiences and resentments, formed long in the past when he had been trained in Russia. The people there were also *mundeles* but of a very different sort. I told them that his suit for Abélé was ended and should now be forgotten. It had just been an excuse for him and a means of getting leverage over me.

They listened in silence and few asked questions. When one of the old biddies muttered something about it all being the outcome of sorcery, thinking she would only be heard by the cronies around her, the Akuamba Kau leaped to his feet and harangued her. He must have had sharp ears, for I was much closer and had caught less than half the old woman's words.

She cringed under his onslaught, feeling the fury of his tongue as if it were a braided whip, and seemed to crumple into a heap where she sat. The Akuamba Kau finished her off by ordering that she return to her house and remain there for the rest of her days. She was forbidden meat and fish and, since she had indirectly accused me of sorcery, she was forbidden to drink water from the springs that I had helped the villagers to make clean and safe. She was condemned now to drink only water from the river that would be brought to her each day by the other old women of her kind.

I thought this sounded harsh and looked at Ekwona to see how he was reacting. He merely shrugged and said, "She is old and losing her mind, that one. He has been kind to her. Another would have banished her to live alone in the forest many days from here, with nobody to bring her food and tend her needs. At least her family will be allowed to care for her through the final months. She is sick, passing blood daily, and has not long left."

"If she is ill, would it not be better to let her have clean water?" I asked. "The river may contain all sorts of bugs and could make her worse."

"That is her problem. She knew these things before she risked the Akuamba Kau's anger," the headman said, and I realised he was right. The villagers had lived with river water as their main source for years before I came. They knew what to do with it. Her family would see that she suffered as little as possible.

The gathering was breaking up now as people dispersed to get on with the tasks they had in hand. I invited the Akuamba Kau to eat with us and received a delighted smile in response. Abélé went to light the cooking fire.

Chapter 15

THE NEXT DAY THE VILLAGE MEN proudly showed me how they had completed the filtration box on our second spring. They had done a good job and knew it, but were pleased to be praised for their work. I suggested we should organise a hunt and have a feast to celebrate it, but they had other ideas.

"We have decided to use all the trees and poles that you cut and build our new meeting-house," Mpwanzu announced proudly. The others all nodded and grinned in agreement. "So, for the next few days, we will collect the last materials and the women will bring thatching. Then we will build."

And so we did. It surprised me to realise that although they had always lived and worked cooperatively, they had now welded into a strong and efficient team, familiar with their environment, sharing their skills to mutual advantage and, above all, having tremendous fun doing so. They had learned many new skills, as I had myself, and they looked for every opportunity to use them. Village life had a new vigour and enthusiasm about it and the smiles on people's faces showed their happiness and the satisfaction this gave them.

The last of the thin tall trees on my future banana patch were

Framework for the new meeting house with piles of rafters + vines ready for the roof.

felled and their roots were removed. Great piles of thatch and palm leaves began to appear around the village. Women sat for hours in chattering, singing groups, braiding fibres and making cord with which to bind the rafters and to secure the thatch. Others wove thick palm leaf mats that would be placed on the rafters before the thatch was laid. Young men returned daily from the forest with great bundles of long thin poles that would become the rafters. By the end of the week materials were piled everywhere and I thought there was enough to build several large houses.

On a bright morning, the construction work began. The headman dug the first hole to take one of the two huge posts that would support the gable ends of the building. After that, relays of men set to and dug other pits. By midday all the supporting posts had been erected, jammed in their holes with rocks and small stones that had been collected by the smaller boys of the village. All these smaller posts were buried top downwards with the tips roasted on a fire, to discourage them from growing. Such was the vigour of many forest plants that poles stuck in the ground could easily sprout and grow new trees.

During the afternoon the long ridge-pole was raised to its lofty perch, supported at each end by a fork on top of the gable posts. Along each of the two long sides slightly thinner poles were bound firmly to the tops of the posts to form the eaves and we began to appreciate the ambitious size of the new meeting-house.

As rafters were laid between the eaves and the ridge, small boys and young men scampered over the developing framework and bound each joint, tightening the bindings with small wooden pegs that were twisted between the fibres and then hammered into the joint. By nightfall almost half of the roof structure was finished.

By noon the next day the whole of the building's framework was complete. Now we could see the impressive size of our new meeting-house. It was massive and could easily accommodate more than double the number of people presently living in the village.

Thatching the roof began as soon as all the bindings had been checked. Large mats of woven palm leaves were laid on the framework and sewn to the poles before huge bundles of thatch were rolled out and laid on top. The thatch was sewn through the matting with long skeins of grass string and tied down to the poles beneath, starting at the eaves and working upwards.

The thatch had a surprisingly complex structure in four layers. First palm matting was laid and sewn on to the rafters. On top of this a thick layer of reed bundles was laid, overlapping with their tips towards the ridge. This was covered by a layer of broad, fan shaped palm fronds with a covering of broad *mongongo* leaves laid like huge tiles pegged over the lot. It took three days for all the thatch to be laid, with a neat double capping of woven palm matting sewn along the ridge. When the eaves were trimmed we had a vast covered space open at the sides and ends. It was airy and surprisingly light under the roof and the scent of the new thatch made it smell clean and fresh.

While working on the springs I had insisted that unused materials and debris should be removed from the working area and was pleased to see that the villagers removed all the off-cuts of wood and thatch from around the new building as they worked. These were piled neatly near one end to be used as fuel in the huge fire pit that was being dug for the inaugural feast.

Once the main structure was complete, the villagers moved inside to scrape the floor level and pack it hard. Others dug a trench round the outside and lined the bottom of it with flat stones from the river. This was intended to catch the rain as it poured from the roof and lead it away down a channel so that the floor inside would remain firm and dry. New clay was brought from the river bank and smeared over the packed floor. Lines of stamping, singing women shuffled backwards and forwards, compacting the clay and burnishing it with their bare feet until it was smooth and shiny and as hard as a well laid slab of concrete.

Two weeks to the day from when we had started, the new meeting-house was finished. Ekwona told me that it must now be left empty and unused for three days. This was to allow the spirits to explore and see that the workmanship was good. If they approved it would be a joyful place and the meetings it housed would be fruitful and harmonious. I did not enquire what would happen if the spirits were dissatisfied, for it was better to leave such questions unasked.

Chapter 16

THE NEXT DAY WE RESTED, doing small tasks around our own homes. Abélé and I spent some time digging in our banana patch, preparing the ground for the new trees and digging the beds to grow peppers and other vegetables.

The day after that the village men brought out their hunting equipment, mended their nets, sharpened spears and made new arrows and strings for their bows. On the morrow, we men would hunt while the women scoured the forest for fruits and roots, edible leaves and berries, and the young boys would go fishing in the river. Even the old and the lame had tasks to perform in preparation for the great feast.

That night the old hag who had been banished to her house by the Akuamba Kau slipped quietly through sleep into the domain of the spirits. Before anyone departed for the hunt, the whole village assembled for the old woman's funeral. These people made little fuss over funerals, but a few simple rituals would be performed to see her on her way into the spirit world. In three days time, her family would start a formal mourning ritual, eating neither meat nor fish nor fruit for two weeks and making small daily offerings to the spirits in the forest round the village. They would wail and cry for two days and then get on with life as though nothing had happened. Dealing with death was a pragmatic business here.

The immediate concern was disposal of the body, but this was a simple process. There was no proper grave; the old woman was carried into the forest and simply laid on the ground in the sacred grove, where her body was covered with her sleeping mat and a pile of sticks and leaves. The denizens of the jungle, animal, insect, fungus and microbes would arrive within hours to recycle her remains. In only a few weeks there would be nothing left but her memory and her spirit would be free to live in the forest with the other ancestors.

Abélé brought an orchid from the forest and placed it over her as we left, and again I was touched by her innate kindness and generosity of spirit. While we were doing this, someone went back to the village and, as tradition demanded, set fire to the old woman's house. By the time we returned it was no more than a smouldering pile of ash.

Mputu had come back from the mill the previous night and joined the other men in the hunting party. He was in high spirits, for the mill engineer had just promoted him to be the second fitter in his maintenance crew. Mpwanzu was justly proud of his son, who was the only wage-earning member of the village.

The hunt was more successful than usual and we returned to the village by late afternoon with one large antelope, a young forest pig, several dik-dik, one monkey, a collection of giant snails, several birds and a few assorted rodents. The boys had also been successful and brought in three large catfish and several baskets of mixed smaller fish. The women's foraging had produced the usual bounteous harvest of fruits and roots, nuts, berries, leaves and palm hearts. By the time we got back to the village, they had started a fire in the communal pit in anticipation of the meat we would bring.

I decided to go down to the river and wash after the long day in our sweaty jungle. As I headed down the path, I saw Mputu talking to Abélé with a slightly conspiratorial air. Both of them wore huge grins and I assumed he was telling her about his promotion. She was always pleased by his achievements and, in her own way, gave him as much encouragement as I did.

The water felt cool and refreshing and I took my time. When I climbed the path again, I thought Mputu had gone, but I saw a pair of feet sticking out from under the Land Rover and guessed he was tinkering with the battered exhaust. I could hear the clink of tools and wondered how many more times it would be possible to repair the old heap before I had to fit a new exhaust.

As I dried and combed my hair, Mputu dragged himself out and came over to where I was sitting, wiping his hands on a rag. "It is mended, Kamran," he said, sitting on the ground, "but you should look for a new pipe. It will not be possible to mend it again."

"Thank you, Mputu. You've done so much work on the machine I should pay you for it," I said.

"You have already paid me. You arranged for me to work at the oil mill."

"Even so I'm grateful for your help. Congratulations on your promotion. I am pleased you are doing so well, and your father is very proud too."

"Éyéee! The work is good and every day I am learning much. It is good that you and my father are happy. You have done much for me, but there is something else I would ask you," the lad replied.

The tone of his voice made me look at him more closely and in the edge of my vision I noticed that Abélé had stopped what she was doing and was watching us. I ignored her and gave Mputu my full attention. "Ask me," I said.

"I am now a man and have a good job that brings money. Even so, my home is here in the village and I hunt with the others and work on our village projects whenever I am here. I have talked with my father and he agrees that it is time to become like other men."

His manner was serious and dignified and I wondered where this was leading. Was he now proposing to move to the town and work in one of the large workshops there, or was he going to live permanently at the oil mill, where presently he only spent two or three nights each week? Again I noticed Abélé watching us. Slowly the truth dawned.

"Ask, Mputu," I said gently. "Mpwanzu is a wise man and he and I are of the same mind."

"I wish to take your daughter for my wife and I ask if you are willing to set *ibene* for her," he replied clearly, so that Abélé too could hear.

I looked at her and had no need to ask if she wished this. Her face showed hope and happiness together and I realised they had discussed the matter in detail, probably many times. Abélé was old for an unmarried girl in this part of the world. Most of them had a child at the breast by her age and, although she had started her cycles later than usual, she was a woman and ready to take a woman's full place in the world.

Turning back to Mputu, I embraced him and said, "Your request pleases me, Mputu. Tonight, in the new meeting-house, you can make your request in front of everyone and I will answer. Yes, I am willing to name the bride price for Abélé. This will be a good thing for the first meeting. Go and tell your father this."

Abélé rushed over and flung her arms around both of us. Such open displays were uncommon among these people and yet, on this occasion, it did not seem so out of place. I left the two laughing together and went into the house to fill the Tilley lamp with fuel for the evening's gathering.

At dusk I lit the lamp and picked up the can of spare fuel. It was going to be another all-night session and the lamp would need to be refuelled before I came home. Everyone was assembling at the meeting-house now so I went off to find Ekwona and tell him what was in store. His face crinkled with pleasure when he heard the news, and he chuckled throatily.

"This is an interesting development, my friend. We will wait until everyone has eaten before anything is said. I am pleased for you, Mputu is a good boy. Did you know of this before?"

"I wondered about it some days ago, but with everything else that was going on, I didn't really give it much thought."

"That is probably a good thing for it has given them time to work it out before asking you," he chuckled again. "The Akuamba Kau told me this would happen."

"How did he know?" I asked, and received again that look that said I should have known better than to ask such a question. The knowledge and insight of such a man is not to be questioned. I accepted the silent admonition with a wry smile. "He will be here tonight?"

"Éyéee, he is always here at times of great importance," he said, and we walked together to join the throng of people assembled in front of the new building.

I felt a small hand slip into mine as Abélé found me in the crowd and I squeezed it and looked down into her smiling face. At the same moment, the Akuamba Kau emerged from the darkness of the meeting-house. He wore no leather hat tonight. Instead his hair was plaited with hundreds of brightly coloured feathers. His pierced ears also supported small bunches of iridescent plumes and around his neck he wore a stout thong with a long iron bell hanging from it. Without his usual clothing of skins, his nakedness was covered by a loincloth of finely woven raffia and I saw that his body was covered by thousands of small scars in intricate swirling patterns interwoven with tattoos of red and blue lines.

His appearance brought instant silence as we all stood and watched. He reached into the shadows behind him and picked up a gourd from which he sprinkled some liquid as he walked round the outside of the new building. The whole village followed stamping rhythmically in the foundation steps of a dance.

When he arrived back at his starting point the witch doctor laid down the gourd and began to dance. He beat vigorously on his iron bell, chanting strange words which had no meaning for the rest of us but which, I assumed, were intelligible to the spirits whose approval and protection he was invoking. For an old man – he must have been over fifty, which was very old in the forest – he was remarkably agile and leaped high in the air from time to time, landing as lightly as a cat and continuing his gyrations without pause.

I noticed a subtle throbbing in the air and thought at first that it was distant thunder. Then I saw that the village drummers had taken up their instruments and picked up the beat of the witch doctor's steps, tapping lightly with their finger tips to lend a subtle quality to their accompaniment. As his steps became more energetic so the beat increased and the sound swelled. Voices joined in and soon all the villagers were singing the praises of their guardian spirits and asking their protection for the new meeting-house.

The new meeting house — The scene of
Mputu's declaration and where Abéle's
idene was named.

Abruptly there was silence and all movement ceased. It was as if
the choreography was cued and yet I was aware of no signal. The
Akuamba Kau turned and entered the meeting house calling out,
"Enter, enter, this house is blessed, enter." Led by Ekwona, the
villagers filed in and at that moment the first drops of the evening
rain clattered on the new thatch and splattered onto the clear
ground where we had all been dancing.

Meat that had been roasting all afternoon was brought from the
fire pit by the women. Baskets and bowls of mashed yams and
manioc porridge were passed round. Children brought fruit and
small fish, grilled over hot coals and the evening turned to feasting.
Usually the men and the women sat separately in the meeting
house, but tonight there was no order to the way people were
grouped, we just sat down together with those who had been
beside us as we entered. Somehow those distributing the food still
managed to observe the order of precedence which normally

prevailed in the village. I noticed that Abélé was with the other women, carrying baskets of meat, and Mputu, when I found him in the throng, was seated with his father and they both looked happy.

After a while Ekwona caught my eye and signalled for me to join him where he sat on a wooden bench at the centre of one of the long sides of the building. This was, I remembered, the traditional place for the headman. The Akuamba Kau was seated on the ground a few feet to his left, which surprised me slightly. I mentioned it to Ekwona and he explained that it was forbidden for the Akuamba Kau to sit anywhere but on the bare earth when inside the meeting-house. By tradition his position was always two arms' length to the left of the headman. I noticed that he was still treated with great respect and the women brought him the best pieces of meat and other things he was known particularly to like.

Conversation was lively while the food was being eaten, with people occasionally getting up and joining other groups. The smallest children scampered through the crowd, having food pushed into their mouths at every group they encountered, and being given sips of palm wine from the numerous gourds that were circulating. The women must have been preparing this unobtrusively for days, I thought, and then realised that even Abélé had prepared some, for I had seen the two large pots standing inside the doorway of our house and smelled the distinctive aroma as I prepared the lamp.

Lamps were hung from the rafters all round the huge shelter and there were so many that the scene inside was quite brightly lit. There were no dark corners and, as the palm matting that underlay the thatch was pale and new, it reflected the light back down onto the people below. It was a happy gathering and every face wore a smile.

Some time later I noticed that although most people had finished eating, there was still mountains of food left. Ekwona told me we would eat again later and there would be very little left by morning. "Then nobody will need to eat for several days," I commented and he laughed.

Reaching down behind the bench, Ekwona picked up a small drum. He beat it sharply with a stick to produce a tattoo that ended the swell of conversation. He stood up and looked round the assembled villagers.

"This house was built by everyone in the village and so belongs to all. It holds a piece of the spirit of each of us and now," he gestured to the Akuamba Kau, still seated in his place, "it has been inspected and blessed by the spirits of the forest. Let it be a place of happiness, not strife. Let it be a place for discussion, not argument. Let it be a place where disagreements are resolved so that those who leave its shelter may do so as friends." He clapped his hands and with one voice the villagers answered him "Éyéee! Let it be so."

"There is one in our village who has made a request of Kamran, who sits here beside me. Kamran has said he will give his answer to that request tonight, in this place, for all to hear," Ekwona announced as the people again fell silent. Then he resumed his seat beside me and picked up a bowl of palm wine that had been left at his feet. He drank and passed the bowl to me. As I lifted it to my lips I saw Mputu weaving his way through the mass of seated bodies towards me and the people nearest shuffled aside a little to make space for him at my feet.

The whole place fell silent again and I deliberately counted slowly to ten before speaking. "Mputu, son of Mpwanzu, you have told me that you wish to take Abélé, my daughter, as your wife and you have asked if I am willing to set *ibene* for her. Is this so?"

"It is so. That is my request," he replied and the village sighed softly.

I was aware of Abélé just behind me and I turned to her. I had no need to ask her, but after all that had gone on in recent weeks I felt that her public agreement would be a good thing. I caught the Akuamba Kau's eye and realised that he thought so too. "Abélé, do you wish me to name your bride price to this man?" I asked loudly.

"I wish it, Papa," she answered equally clearly, and I wondered briefly if she had been off into the forest to practice so that she could make her declaration without faltering.

I turned back to Mputu and looked him in the eyes. "I hear your request and name the bride price for my daughter as follows," I began. "You will bring clay from the river and fashion two *akwali* with close fitting wooden lids. In the space in front of my house, you will make a fire to bake them for three days until they are cured. On the day I give my daughter to you, I shall bury these beside the door of the house where she will live so that she will always have clean water to give you and to drink herself.

"You will take raffia from the palm trees beside my house and use it to weave six *ikobio* as a sign of your payment. One of these I will place in the roof of the house where my daughter will live, as a sign of my blessing on your marriage.

"There is a piece of hardwood that stands by the door of my house; you will take this and cut it in two. From each piece you will carve the image of one of the forest animals. One of these Abélé shall keep for her children. The other will be mine so that I have a toy to bring laughter to the face of my daughter's first-born child.

"You will cut poles and thatch in the forest and use them to build a good thatched roof over the fireplace beside my house, where Abélé does her cooking, so that she may do so without the fire being drowned by the rain.

"All these things you will do with the duty and respect that a son should give to his father, to show that you are worthy, for on the day I give you my daughter as your wife, you will become my son. These things you will do within the time of the next two new moons from today."

This covered the part of *ibene* that I had specified last when I had named the bride price for Abélé before, since it was, in fact, the most important element.

"In addition to these things," I continued, "you will provide a strong tin box for my daughter to store her possessions in, and one length of coloured cotton cloth of the type called *ikende*. You will provide a fine new machete, one metal cooking pot, two large and two small enamel food bowls from the market. All these things are to be done before two new moons have passed if this thing is to be." I paused again and looked around the sea of attentive faces.

"On the day when I give my daughter to you as your wife, you will roast a fowl for me so that your new father will have a full belly to stop him thinking about his loss." This brought a ripple of laughter from the villagers and a smile to Mputu's otherwise impassive face. "This is *ibene* I ask you to pay for my daughter Abélé. I ask all in this house to hear this and judge if it be fair."

"The price is good, the price is fair," the villagers chanted in unison and again fell silent, waiting to hear Mputu's response.

"You ask too little," Mputu issued the formal challenge, indicating that he found it acceptable.

"Even so, that is the bride price I ask."

"I would pay more."

"It is what I ask, nothing more."

"Then I accept and will pay as you ask. Let all the people here be witness," he declared loudly, and leaned forward to kiss my knee.

I took the bowl of palm wine that Ekwona was offering, drank and passed the bowl to Mputu. He drank and passed it back. Twice more each of us drank from the bowl and the bargain was sealed. Talk among the villagers resumed immediately and the Akuamba Kau stood up and shook each of us by the hand.

"This is a good thing and a fair price," he said, giving our bargain his blessing also.

Mputu went off to inform his father formally about the bargain he had struck, even though he had heard it all. The Akuamba Kau touched me lightly on the arm to keep my attention. I was still holding the bowl of palm wine, so I offered it to him. He drank and passed it back. As I drank again he told me that Nkwanu Knaii would bring his family the next day. "It is a pity he was not here tonight," I said, "but there was not time to tell him."

"He knows," the wise man said with a glint in his eye. "But he could not be here tonight. This night is normally forbidden to people who are not of this village. He was only permitted to be here before because that man was a Party official and, as you will recall, he was hidden."

I should have realised this, for Ekwona would have invited him if his presence had been appropriate. The Party was important, being the political foundation of the whole country, and it was represented at all normal events, but tonight was a private village matter.

In Nkwanu Knaii's case his presence was normally doubly welcome as he was popular with everyone in the sector. I wondered for a moment how it was that he already knew but thought it better just to accept the fact and not ask. Reading my mind the Akuamba Kau smiled his agreement and moved off to talk to other people.

Mpwanzu came over and shook my hand. "Well, my brother, that was an interesting surprise. But for the gold, the price was almost the same and yet there is no hard burden in it," he laughed.

"The price was unpayable for the other man, for all that it was fair," I said. "For Mputu it is a price he will pay with pride and in the paying he will honour Abélé and ensure her status. The gold was just a sop to the other man's vanity, something to distract his attention from the real price. For Mputu, it would be an unfair burden, for even as he earns money, he is still not rich. Also he is not taking a woman from this village to live in another place."

Before either of us could say anything else, a basket of meat was thrust between us.

"Will my two fathers accept meat from a dutiful daughter?" Abélé asked with a saucy grin.

"We will," we said, each taking a piece. "But go and find Mputu, he has much to discuss with you and the skies are clear, the moonlight beckons," Mpwanzu told her, and she hurried off to do his bidding.

OTHERS CAME TO OFFER THEIR approval and we moved around talking to people and hearing their kind words and praise for Abélé. How far she has come in under a year, I thought; from outcast waif to respected young woman, and soon to be a bride. Well, I would not be able to stay here forever. Perhaps another nine months or a year and the job I came to do in the surrounding villages would be done and I would be needed elsewhere. Abélé would need someone else in her life then. With Mputu beside her, and

Mpwanzu and his wife in the background, she would be more than well situated. Her association with me had given her status, enhanced by the Akuamba Kau's obvious approval and his liking for her food. Now Mputu, whose position at the oil mill made him a significant figure in the life of the village, would improve her position still further.

To add to that, Abélé was now quite proficient in French and she could read and write quite well. It occurred to me then that I had previously talked to the head of the main school in Kikwit and asked his help in getting her education recognised. He had agreed that she could sit the school exams and had even lent me a number of books for her. These she had devoured and then read again and again. I needed to talk to him once more and see when the examinations were to be held. I would discuss the matter with Nkwanu Knaii tomorrow when he brought his family to visit.

With the clearing of the night sky, some of the villagers had gone outside and the drummers had taken up their drums. Dancing was now in progress with separate lines of men and women conducting a dialogue of stamping gyrations and rhythmic chants in time to the insistent and compelling beat. I listened for a moment and thought how different it was from the modern vogue in Western music where the heavy throb of the base made one's liver shake and rattled a person's wits with its dominating, monotonous pulse. This had variety woven into the basic rhythm with subtle susurrations of softly caressed drum skins giving harmony to the more percussive elements.

The dancers' movements too had artistry in them, being expressive and suggestive, blatant and yet subtle, illustrating and enhancing the relationship between the people and the forest they inhabited. It was a form of expression almost absent from my own culture and I envied these folk with whom I was privileged to work and share this place.

Masks representing the forest spirits and the essence of the ancestors had been bought out and now adorned some of the dancers. Others sported coats and costumes made of raffia and decorated with feathers and a few shells. The whole thing took on a carnival air. I went out to sit by the fire and watch, but friendly hands took hold and drew me into the dance. A few cautious steps, friendly, laughing guidance from my neighbours and various shouts of encouragement, then I gave myself up to the moment and accepted the rhythm. It was not, after all, the first time that I had danced with my friends, and knew well enough what to expect. From time to time dancers would drop out for a few minutes to drink or just to rest briefly before rejoining.

After a while I took a break and found myself sharing a gourd of cool water with Olidange.

"They will want you to dance the story of the man from Kimwamwa," he said, and seeing my look of alarm, continued. "It is our way of telling the spirits that we know the truth and have nothing to be ashamed of, nothing to fear, and nothing for which to seek revenge. You have nothing to worry about, others will help." And so it was a few minutes later when I rejoined the line.

Unseen hands pushed me forwards as the drummers changed their beat and I could almost feel my fingers dismantling the Tilley lamp. A huge figure, wrapped in a gaudy, padded shirt, wearing a grotesque round mask approached and danced around me taunting. I moved in response, squirming and wheeling, seeking a means of escape until the huge figure slapped his hand on the ground and stood defiant.

On the dance went, telling the tale; the conference, the

confrontation and the bride price, the rejection and the scorn, and the big man's departure. Then others joined in and we were doing normal things until the panting messenger came. The long car journey through the night with Nkwanu Knaii and our arrival in Kimwamwa; others recounted the villagers' hunt and Kuloni Nkese's capture and return to Kimwamwa; his punishment, the revelling mob and the hideous head on a pole overlooking his own funeral feast were all portrayed and that evil man was finally consigned to oblivion.

I wanted to stop, to forget, but the dance had energy of its own and would not let me go. As the gruesome story was enacted again, part of me relived the horror while another part looked on at the beauty of the scene and the expressive fluency of the dancers.

The tale moved on. Once more I was back in this village recounting the tale, then off to town and home again. The meeting house was built and Mputu presented his suit, for the second time tonight I named Abélé's bride price for the young man, in mime and movement this time, not with words.

I have no idea where the dance steps came from unless the spirits moved me, but the next day I was told by the Akuamba Kau that this had been one of the most vivid re-enactments he had seen. I know only that I was taken completely by the moment and could not have stopped if I had wanted to.

But this was now a tale of joy; why stop? It was a celebration of my daughter and her betrothed; it was the honour of the village people who had entrusted Abélé to my care. At last the tale was done and the dance ended. It had taken almost two hours and I should have been exhausted, but somehow felt light and rested. It had been therapeutic as well as exciting. Catharsis, I realised, can come in unexpected forms and I understood that the ghost of

Kuloni Nkese had been presented to the spirits and was now finally exorcised. It would cause no nightmares in the future. There would be no hidden legacy for Abélé or any of our friends who had unwillingly been involved.

A new dance started and I retired inside the meeting-house and sat down with Ekwona and Mpwanzu. They had been discussing my bride price and were intrigued by how virtually the same bride price could have such different implications.

"One thing I am curious to know," Mpwanzu asked, "is why you did not demand that Mputu build a house of his own? It is usual for a bride to move to her husband's house when she is married."

"And so she will," I smiled. "You know that I shall not be able to stay here for ever. When all the work is finished, the people who sent me will want me to go elsewhere and my house will be empty. On the day before I hand her over, I shall give Mputu my house and take Abélé to the town. When she returns in the morning it will be to her husband's own house. He helped in rebuilding that house for me when I first came here. I have asked him to build a good roof over the cooking place and he has enough to do without building another house. He worked with us all on building this meeting place. Mputu has already demonstrated he can do these things. Is this acceptable to the village?"

"It is," Ekwona said. "The house was dead before you came, and Mputu was one of those who helped give it life again. He has therefore built a house, so the requirement is met."

"Éyéee, you are a cunning one, Kamran," Mpwanzu said in a long drawn out sigh. "Kuloni Nkese never stood a chance against you, but he was too stupid to realise it. Are you sure you are not *niseke?*"

"He is not," said a soft voice from the shadows, and we all turned to see the Akuamba Kau quietly observing us. "But he has eaten *nguakua* and shared it with his chief. His understanding is great"

"Éyéee!" my companions all responded in unison. I glanced at Ekwona and saw the pleasure in his eyes at being described as my chief.

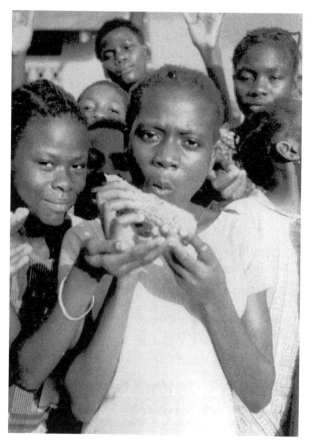

Abélé after her exams.

Chapter 17

DAWN CAME AND EVENTUALLY I retired to my house to sleep. Abélé was already there, curled up on her mat under the deeply overhanging eaves. I was touched that she felt safe now and need not hide inside where it was often stuffy and airless.

I was woken by Abélé before midday and went down to the river to wash. Coming back up the path, I heard familiar voices and the delighted squeals of small children. Our friends from town had arrived and were being welcomed by Abélé. "I hear you've at last found a good husband for your daughter," Nkwanu Knaii said, as I joined them.

"I see your information service is as good as ever," I laughed, and sat down to tell him about the previous day's events. Abélé and Akanku were in a huddle by the cooking fire, their eyes bright with excitement, exchanging women's news.

I noticed then that there was an appetising aroma in the air and felt hungry. By the smell of it, Abélé had been making curry with meat left over from the feast, and I realised she must have been awake for some time before me. The food was soon ready and we sat down to eat. The children had fresh coconut milk added to their bowls to take the sting out of the spices, but they too ate with enjoyment.

After the meal I dragged out the three oil drums that were stored behind the house and we rolled them down to the beach beside the river. I had saved some of the poles from the banana patch and enough rope to bind them together into a triangular raft. Abélé had woven a thick palm fibre mat the previous week. This we laced to the top as a deck, and soon the raft was finished. With another long rope from one corner tied firmly to the bank, we launched the strange looking craft and it floated out into the river on the end of its tether.

Naked children plunged in after it and swarmed aboard. Wrapped in simple cloth sarongs, Abélé and Akanku joined them and made sure that the younger ones did not do anything too foolhardy, while Nkwanu and I swam lazily round to pick up any who fell off into the current.

Other children in the village, hearing the noise, came and joined the fun. We spent a merry afternoon playing in the water and sitting on the beach chatting.

Later the two women went back up to the house to prepare more food, so I untied the raft and Nkwanu and I paddled it out into the river and poled our way upstream with a gang of children on board and more following in the water. We went just round the bend and then let the current bring us back. At last we hauled the raft onto the beach, tied its rope to the fig tree, reclaimed our dry clothes and went back to the house.

After supper I mentioned to Nkwanu the ideas I had about entering Abélé for the school exams in town. He thought it an excellent idea and asked to see the books she had been using. He chatted to her for a while in French and then looked at her written work. "It is good," he told me, "she has learned well. Go and speak to the school teacher soon. The exams are not far off."

Nkwanu and his family had agreed to stay a few days with us, so the following morning we organised a small expedition into the forest to collect suckers from the wild trees and plant our banana patch. With Abélé in the lead, shepherding the older children, and Akanku carrying Admi, we set off on a well-used path. After a while I took the lead because Abélé, despite all her forest knowledge, did not know where to find the grove of pink bananas I had located.

There were game trails that took us close to the spot and it was only necessary to hack our way though a few yards of heavy tangled undergrowth before we found the trees. Some of them bore ripe fruit and the children fell on these with delight, while Nkwanu and I dug up the suckers and stacked them in our baskets.

On the way back Abélé collected a number of orchid stems. They were mostly gaudy and fragrant, but I made her leave one behind, despite it being the most beautiful, because it smelled like carrion. As we walked Akanku gathered nuts and berries. She wanted to add these to our larder but Abélé told her she should save them and take them back to the town. "We only have to walk into the forest to collect more," she insisted.

That evening I took my friend over to inspect the new meeting-house and he was most impressed with it. "There are many advantages to living here, Kamran," he observed. "I wish my job permitted me to do the same, but unfortunately I am tied to the town. Now I have more responsibility as the Party have added Kimwamwa to my sector and I shall have to work harder."

"The people of Kimwamwa are fortunate then," I observed. "And I am sure you will soon find good assistants to represent you there."

He agreed that it would not be a problem and asked if I could visit the village again as they badly needed a clean water supply. I agreed to go soon and asked if there had been any fallout from the unfortunate events that had happened there. He told me the authorities had accepted his report and the regional director had heaved a great sigh of relief at being freed from his most troublesome burden.

When our friends were ready to return to the town, Abélé loaded the Toyota with baskets of fruit and bundles of other forest produce. She produced a huge roll of new palm matting, which we tied onto the roof and baskets containing all sorts of odds and ends she wanted her big sister, as Akanku had now become, to take home with her. When I remarked on the amount and variety of the gifts, Abélé merely shrugged and said, "There has been plenty of time to make things, and I wanted Akanku to have them. She has given me so much. It is a small return."

"It is more than that, Abélé, and you know it. Akanku was born in the forest and misses it greatly because she has to live in the town. It was very thoughtful of you."

"It is nothing. She is my sister," was the only reply I got.

Two days later, we went to the town ourselves, to visit the school. The teacher was impressed with Abélé's work and agreed that she could sit the examinations in two weeks time. If she passed, she would receive a certificate. He made a number of helpful suggestions and Abélé wrote them down in her notebook. As soon as we got home she brought out her books and for the next two weeks spent every spare moment working at them and insisting that I speak only French to her.

On the appointed day, I left her at the school and went to the market. All day long while waiting, I found my thoughts going back to her. It was a frustrating day, my mind unsettled and anxious, and

I gnawed a thumbnail down to nothing. When I went to collect her in the afternoon, Abélé came out wearing a huge smile.

"It was fun!" she announced when I asked her how it had gone. The results would come out the following week.

Meanwhile, back in the village we saw a great deal of Mputu. He brought a huge mound of clay from the river and produced two solid, well-crafted *akwali*. Abélé helped him by tending the fire while they were curing as he had to return to work at the oil mill for a day. She also stripped the raffia palms and prepared the materials from which he wove his *ikobio*. The heavy log that had stood by the door for months disappeared and Abélé told me he had taken it to the mill to cut it in half in the workshop. I hoped the manager would not object, but she said Mputu had asked permission first.

Abélé had collected broad leaves from the forest and a pile of thatch for the cooking shelter and she spent an afternoon working with Mputu building the framework for the roof. Mputu cut four stout poles with forks at the top and set them in the ground. Together they lifted the roof frame into place and bound it tightly to the corner posts. It stood like that for a week before the thatch was put on.

A week after our visit to the school, I was talking to Ekwona one afternoon when the school teacher arrived on his putt-putt motorcycle. The exam results were good, he confided, and Abélé had passed them all. I asked when she would receive her certificate. That was the reason for his visit, he announced. He had come specially to present it to her. Ekwona suggested he should wait until the evening and we would call the villagers to the meeting-house. The teacher agreed and went off with Ekwona. I went home but said nothing to Abélé.

That evening I took her over to the meeting-house and she was excited to find the teacher there. I noticed that Mputu was also present and felt pleased that he would be there to share Abélé's moment. He more than shared it, as it turned out, it was his moment too. Without any of us knowing, the manager at the oil mill had been coaching him during the evenings he spent there. The manager had put him in for the literacy exam and told him to say nothing. He too had passed and to thunderous applause from the villagers he received his certificate alongside Abélé.

It was a time of pride for the village and great happiness for me, not to mention the two youngsters. The Akuamba Kau, whom we had not seen for some time, emerged from the forest just as the presentation was about to be made, and I saw him standing in the shadows, smiling like a wrinkled guardian angel. It was slightly disconcerting how he appeared like that, at significant moments, but I had ceased to wonder how he did it and how he knew when to turn up. He was *niseke*, so it was better just to accept it.

Chapter 18

THE SECOND NEW MOON WAS three days away when Mpwanzu came and asked me to go with him to the meeting-house. "My son is ready to pay the bride price," he told me.

Again the villagers were assembled and Mputu had brought meat that was roasting in the fire pit. This time the men and women sat separately, at opposing ends of the meeting house. With the Akuamba Kau on the ground to his left, Ekwona was seated on his headman's bench and signalled for me to join him. As I took my place, Mputu rose and the meeting-house fell silent.

"I have come to pay the bride price that you asked for your daughter," Mputu announced. "I ask these people and our chief to witness that the price is paid in full so I may claim my bride." He looked round the gathering and the villagers told him they would witness it. From under a large pile of matting, Mputu brought two huge pots. They were not only finely made, but decorated round the top with engraved patterns and had beautifully carved wooden lids.

"You asked me for two *akwali*, so that your daughter would have somewhere to store clean water for her house. These I have made," he said, placing the pots on the floor at my feet.

"It is paid," intoned the witnesses.

"You asked me for six *ikobio*, as a sign that that your daughter would always have furnishings for her home," he lifted the rolled mats high for everyone to see their ends plaited in the traditional manner, before placing them at my feet.

"It is paid," the villagers repeated.

"You asked me for carved animals, so that your daughter's children would have toys to play with and her father would have something to delight his first grandchild." Once again he held the two carvings high, to be viewed by everyone, then placed them before me. One was a red spotted monkey and the other an *okapi*.

"It is paid," the audience chanted again.

"You asked me for a metal box, so your daughter would have somewhere safe to keep her possessions," he said, placing a large tin trunk beside the other items.

Red spotted monkey carved by Mputu.

There was a general sigh of surprise from the audience and I could see at once that it was not the usual sort of tin box that I had expected, such as was sold in the town market. This was something special. It was finely finished and burnished, the entire surface covered with finely worked patterns representing all the traditional shapes and designs of the forest, and I wondered where it had come from and at what cost. I had not intended this to be a costly item.

"Éyéee, it is paid," said the villagers, with admiration.

Each of the other items was produced with similar ceremony and presented. Each time the villagers gave their approval as the items were laid on the floor before me.

"You asked for a roof over your cooking fire so that the fire should not be put out by the rain," Mputu said. "It is done and all have seen it."

"It is paid," the chorus agreed.

Mputu came and sat in front of me, leaned forward and kissed my knee. "I pay these things you have asked with the respect due from a son to his father. I ask you to accept them as payment of *ibene* as it was named," he asked formally.

"I see all the things that you have brought, and they are good," I gave the formal response. "The payment is accepted, the bride price is paid."

"Éyéee! The bride price is paid," the villagers chanted and Mputu appeared to grow an inch with the satisfaction of the moment. He was about to leave when I held up my hand to stop him.

"There is still one more thing that must be done," I said. "You have no house of your own, so where am I to deliver my daughter?"

The meeting house was silent with expectation and even the forest seemed to hold its breath.

"You helped to rebuild my house when I first came here; you helped to build this place, and now you have made a fine roof over my cooking fire. By these things you have shown that you can provide my daughter with a home. Mputu, I give you my house as a marriage gift. Now I know where to deliver your bride when the new moon rises and maybe, sometimes, I shall claim shelter in your house."

"Éyéee! it is given!" the villagers shouted.

Food was brought then and the village had another party. We ate and sang and danced until dawn and retired happily to sleep away the morning. During the evening I spoke to Mputu and asked him where he had found the trunk. With pride in his eyes he told me that the engineer at the oil mill was teaching him to work metal and had permitted him to make it in the workshop. I told him the decorations were beautiful and saw the happiness in his eyes.

At noon the next day, Abélé and I climbed into the Land Rover and went to the town. With pride, and more than a little dramatic licence, Abélé told Akanku and Nkwanu Knaii how Mputu had paid the bride price and we toasted the morrow with cool beer. I asked our friends if they would come down to the village next day to share our celebration and they happily accepted.

In the morning, I went with Abélé to the market to buy new clothes for her wedding, and we called at the store and bought many crates of bottled beer for the feast that would follow. We went back to Akanku's house and she dressed Abélé in her new garments, tossing the old ones onto the fire saying they were the clothes of childhood and should not be worn again.

We all set off together, the Toyota leading, and went back to Inkwiti to launch Abélé into her new life. As we came into the village, I was amazed to see the national flag hanging from a tall pole. Every house had bright forest flowers strewn over the roof, and there was an air of excitement about the place.

I parked beside the meeting-house and went inside to where the things Mputu had paid were still laid out on the floor. As the sun slipped deep into the western forest, I picked up the two huge water pots, admiring again the workmanship, and took them to Mputu's house. Digging a large hole against the bottom of the wall I buried them to their necks in the ground on the opposite side of the door to the pots we had used before. Into each one I poured clean water from a gourd one of the neighbours had brought.

I went back to the meeting house where Abélé was waiting and we loaded the cloth and other things into the trunk, leaving only one small carving of a red spotted monkey and five *ikobio* on the floor. As Abélé hoisted the trunk onto her head, I took the sixth *ikobio* and led her back to the house. Mputu was now waiting in the doorway. Most of the village had gathered outside to watch.

"The moon is new," he challenged as we approached. "The bride price is paid and accepted. I demand my bride."

"The moon is new, *ibene* has been paid and accepted. I give you your bride," I answered him, taking Abélé by the hand and placing it in his.

He stood aside and helped Abélé lower her heavy trunk to the ground as I entered the house.

"This *ikobio* I put in your roof as a sign of my blessing on your home," I called, pushing the rolled raffia mat firmly between the rafters and the thatch above the doorway. "I ask the spirits of this place to watch over you and keep peace in this house."

Mputu led Abélé inside and she looked around, her eyes opening wide with surprise for Mputu had given the whole house a coat of whitewash and it was bright and clean.

I walked out and closed the door firmly behind me, my part in the formalities was done for the time being. It struck me that as a way of getting married, this was far easier than the mumbo-jumbo encrusted way of some cultures, particularly those that shrouded marriage with religious significance. Here it was a practical process. The spirits had been propitiated by the payment of *ibene* and would be involved later as we feasted and danced to celebrate the couple's union.

The crowd outside cheered, hands grasped mine and greetings were exchanged. I saw, as expected, the Akuamba Kau looking on, always part of this village and yet not of it. He had instructed me on the ritual of the occasion and I went over to thank him. Together we walked back to the meeting-house.

One of the villagers asked me where I would live now. "With my brother Mpwanzu, of course," I laughed. "But I have work to do in some of the other villages as well as here. Now I am asked to go and help clean the water in Kimwamwa. I shall go there tomorrow for two weeks. Then if a dutiful son and daughter should invite me to stay with them in their house, who knows?"

"Éyéee, they will ask you," my friends said, and I knew it would be so.

From the meeting house I collected the remaining *ikobio* and the carving and took them to Mpwanzu's house where the rest of my few possessions had been moved. The village gathered again in the meeting house, food was brought in and with renewed banter the village settled down to another feast. This was becoming a habit, I thought.

MPUTU AND HIS BRIDE JOINED us two hours later, both looking flushed and pleased with themselves. Abélé came over to where I sat with Nkwanu Knaii and a group of other friends. She embraced and hugged me tightly. "Thank you, Papa."

"It is good?" I asked.

"Éyéee! It is good, Papa, and he is gentle and kind."

"Then I am well pleased. Now I will bring the beer from the Land Rover so that we may celebrate properly." I went outside to where the vehicle was parked and found willing hands to help unload. As the last crate was passed, I found the Akuamba Kau at my elbow.

"A word with you, my friend," he said, leading me out into the darkness where the forest bordered the village.

I followed and stopped when he indicated, sitting on a fallen log beside him.

"Is there a problem?" I asked, wondering why else he should choose to talk in this private manner.

"There is no problem. It is another matter I wish to talk to you about," he said with a serious tone. "I am an old man, my friend, and old bones do not last forever. My time is almost done and when I go from this place it will be for the last time. In due course another will come to replace me. I ask you to say nothing until it is done."

"This saddens me, my friend," I told him. "I have noticed for some weeks that you appeared tired. Now I understand, but I'm pleased you are here tonight. Will you invoke the spirits and bless them?"

"I will. The spirits will favour them, for I have already seen beyond. Soon I too will be in their ranks and shall watch with kindness. Abélé has been blessed with two good fathers. The first was a fine doctor, a good seer, and a kind man. The second has been a good teacher, a strong protector, and has given her happiness."

"You have been a good guide to me," I said, "I thank you for this, and hope I have done as you expected."

"You understand that because of who I am it would not have been right for me to act directly? It has not been needed, for your heart was as mine. You have done as I would have chosen and more. Come now, we will return and invoke the spirits to bless your *ibene* and the payment of it. You will please an old man by dancing one more time to celebrate this day. Afterwards I shall go."

As we walked back a question came to my mind and I said, "May I ask one more thing?" He nodded his consent so I continued. "Abélé's first father, who was he?"

"He was a wise man. But for all that he would be well pleased, as I am, with what you have done. He could not have done it, but you listened to men's hearts as well as to their words. You found and ate *nguakua* and used well the understanding it gave. He was my son."

"Thank you." I held out my hand and he brushed it lightly with his gnarled fingertips.

The celebration went on non-stop for three days. I danced with the others to celebrate Abélé's new life with Mputu and I danced again to honour the old man.

Nobody saw him go, but I knew the moment of his leaving for I felt a sharp jolt of separation. Some time later I found Ekwona, staring blankly into the forest behind the meeting house.

"I share your sadness," I told him, realising that both of us had tears in our eyes. "He was a wonderful man."

"He has been a good friend to this village," Ekwona said, turning to face me. "To have two such sons, a man is blessed, but it was your bride price and the way you dealt with the man from Kimwamwa that pleased him most. Now he is at peace with the world."

Postscript

THESE EVENTS ALL TOOK PLACE in the mid-1970s when Mobutu's regime had been in power for about twelve years. While he had undoubtedly consolidated his power base and enriched himself personally from the national treasury, neither he nor his rapacious cohorts had yet embarked on the wholesale rape and plundering of the nation's resources that characterised the last ten years of his reign. During the time I was in Zaïre, the rule of law still applied; a few individuals, like Kuloni Nkese, were venal in the extreme, but for the most part, officials, policemen and civil servants still took pride in doing their work without being bribed. They were, of course, being paid and most were riding the wave of political involvement that fuelled Mobutu's "authenticity" programme and his stated intention to create a sense of national identity among the 273 tribes (Mobutu's count) that made up Zaïre.

Our area, in southern Bandundu, had been peaceful since the civil war that followed independence ended in 1963. The villagers were inclined to resolve their differences through public shouting matches, in marked contrast to the more violent, machete-wielding habits of the tribes in the more prosperous and populated eastern provinces. In 1997 all that changed. By then things were beginning to collapse. The economy had been ruined by Mobutu's plundering fat cats, few government employees ever received any pay and corruption and bribery became the norm. To the forest dwellers, this meant little for they lived largely outside the monetary economy, but there were others with heavy ambitions.

Led by Laurent Kabila, revolution started in the eastern provinces, supported by Rwandan troops, Ugandan mercenaries and tribesmen from Shaba and Bukavu provinces with appetites for violence. Mobutu was forced from power and went into exile in Morocco. Soon afterwards, the country changed its name to the Democratic Republic of Congo. Democracy, however, was insubstantial and quickly abandoned as the country became nothing more than the battleground of greedy warlords and foreign mercenaries.

Civil war again erupted, leaving no area untouched. Marauding rebels swept through the country slaughtering anyone who was either ethnically 'wrong' or who opposed them. Whole communities were wiped out, their villages razed to a patch of smouldering ash, their fields and food stores pillaged and anything that resembled infrastructure laid waste. Since all this started in 1997, it is estimated that more than four million people have died.

The forest area may have been inaccessible, but it was far from immune from all the trouble. The palm oil mill where Mputu worked was sacked early in 1998 and all the nearby villages were reported to have been destroyed. A few of the people may have escaped into the jungle, but I have not been able to establish contact with anyone since then. Even Kikwit, which was a prosperous, bustling town in 1975, is now nothing more than a war-torn wreck with a much-diminished population eking out an uncertain existence in grinding, lawless poverty. This has now become the norm all over that vast country which covers an area larger than western Europe and which, if properly managed and led, could have been the engine room of Africa.

Despite extensive enquiries through all sorts of channels, I have found no trace of Abélé, Mputu, Ekwona and all the others. I fear that, like countless nameless ones, they all fell victim to the civil war and are now nothing but a treasured memory. I hope they found peace among the forest spirits and their ancestors.

IN LATE 2006, JAMES DARLING asked permission to marry my daughter Nina. In keeping with tradition, I named the bride price for Nina before a dozen witnesses. Although the details were adapted to the modern European context, the bride price was structured in the same traditional way as before. James accepted, paid the price and in August 2008, I delivered him his bride.

Nina and James, 2008.

Glossary

WITH A GREAT DIVERSITY OF languages, the forest peoples of the central African basin have their own names and terms for everything. Many of these do not translate exactly into English (or French) and quite a few are intimately involved in the somewhat less tangible, spiritual aspects of the people's lives. Where necessary I have used some of these words in the text because they fit and nothing else does.

The following notes are offered to help readers make sense of these and relate them to more familiar terms.

akwali – These are large, unglazed, earthenware pots which are buried, shoulder-deep, outside the house. They are generally positioned by the doorway, under the overhanging eaves, to protect them from rain or falling debris. *Akwali* have tightly fitting wooden lids, which are often carved with representations of forest spirits, family totems or the symbols of other guardian beings. The *akwali* are used to store fresh water for drinking and cooking and are designed to keep their contents cool. Each pot holds about 15 *oukwe* (qv) of water.

atelier – A workshop, usually mechanical and often comprising little more than a man with a few tools. Most of the tools would be old, many second-hand, and some even cobbled together by a local blacksmith. However basic, these rudimentary workshops are what keep Africa's rural transport moving. They display tremendous ingenuity and practical skill in making all sorts of unlikely mechanisms work and keep working.

bula – The local name for a type of palm that grows in this part of the forest. It has tough leaves with broad, flat, finger-like leaves that can be split and woven into stiff open baskets to form sieves and strainers. The glossy surface of the leaves makes the finished basket almost non-stick when sieving flour.

colons – White people of the colonial era, mostly Belgian, but some Portuguese and a few French.

dishi – A malign rogue spirit.

dot – One of the terms used for the bride price that is paid by a prospective husband to his bride's father for the purchase of his bride's hand. (See also *ibene*.)

ebugo – The root of a plant growing all over the forest region of Central Africa which is commonly used in initiation ceremonies and other activities involving exceptional access to the spirit world. The root has strong hallucinogenic properties that produce varying effects dependant on the form, manner and amount ingested. These effects almost always involve copious vomiting.

ewo – Taboo

foufou – A thick and heavy starch paste made out of yams, manioc or other tubers and used as a diet staple. Preparation methods vary, but in most the tubers are peeled, washed and boiled or steamed before being pounded into a smooth pulp. This is then cooked again until it becomes like very thick porridge. It is eaten with the fingers, taking a small lump, rolling it around in one hand to form a smooth, bite-sized ball and then pressing a thumb into this to make a pocket to hold sauce or stew. It is then dipped into the communal pot before being put in the mouth.

ibene – Another name for the bride price, used particularly when it is claimed by the father from his prospective son-in-law just before the actual marriage takes place. As well as the price itself, *ibene* also encompasses the terms and conditions of the bride price and the manner in which it is to be paid.

ikende – This was the local name for the cheap, brightly coloured, printed cotton that is commonly available in most markets across Africa. A length in the local markets was normally about twenty-five feet and would have at least ten full repeats of the printed pattern.

ikobio – These are traditional raffia mats which are used exclusively as part of a *dot* (qv) or bride price. They are woven by hand with a thick, stiff palm fibre warp and a fine, pliable raffia weft so that they can be rolled easily in one direction only. Their size is related to the length of the arm of the person making them, measured from the shoulder to the wrist. The warp ends are left long so that they can be plaited when the mat is rolled. They are presented in this form.

The bride's father will unroll one *ikobio*, in order to see the quality of the workmanship. Another will be placed in the rafters of the marital home when the bride is delivered to her new husband. Strictly the bridegroom should make all the *ikobio* himself to demonstrate his skill, but it has become common in recent years for the bride to help prepare these.

kapok tree – A tall hardwood tree (*Eriodendron anfractuosum*) that has a trunk and branches heavily studded with short, sharp thorns. The lowest branches are normally twenty feet or more above ground and the base of the trunk has heavy buttresses rising to six feet or so. These trees produce hundreds of grapefruit-sized seed pods containing a fine downy white fibre (kapok) in which the seeds are embedded.

In many parts of Africa, particularly in the coastal regions of West Africa, kapok trees have special significance to sorcerers and witch doctors, the spaces between their buttresses being used for fetish altars at which to make offerings and sacrifices.

In some places the trunks are used to carve dug-out canoes. This is partly because they provide a suitable length of straight log that is easily worked and buoyant, and also because the tree is deemed to have special mystical properties that make it acceptable for such use.

kubula – This is a volumetric measure for grain, powders or solids. Its origin relates to the capacity of the sieving basket that can be woven from a single frond taken from a particular type of forest palm, whose local name is *bula* (qv). One *kubula* is usually just under one pint: 5 kubula = about 6 pints.

Kubula is also a linear measure that is used for one specific measurement only – the length of *nktuna* (qv), the pestle used for pounding flour or paste in a *kumpunu* (qv). The linear form is derived from the width of the *bula* palm frond whose leaves are used to make sieve baskets. These average about two feet wide at their broadest point.

kumpunu – This is an upright log that has been hollowed out and is used as a mortar for pounding grain into flour or yams into paste. Made of hardwood, a *kumpunu* will generally stand just over knee high. The top half is hollowed out and has a rounded bottom to the bowl. The total capacity of the bowl is about 10 *oukwe* (qv) or just over 20 pints. The pounding volume is generally just under half the full volume, to allow the grain or paste room to move without spilling while being pounded with a long, heavy pestle. The pestle, *nktuna* (qv) is measured in *kubula* (qv) and is generally about three *kubula* long.

mundele – A white man.

nktuna – This is a well-seasoned hardwood log about two *kubula* (qv) long that is used to pound grain or dried tubers into flour and yams, other tubers or leaves into paste. It has a rounded end and the upper part of the shaft is sometimes decorated with incised designs to improve the user's grip. The name derives from the sound this pestle makes as it is hurled downwards into the *kumpunu* (qv) when pounding yams.

nguakua – This is a rare fruit that is believed both to imbue those who find it with special insight and knowledge and also to reveal an individual's special nature by virtue of being found. It grows on a nondescript vine to about the size of a goose egg and may vary in colour from yellow to pink to pale green. It has an irregular, knobbly skin with an outside texture like fine, unglazed Morocco leather. The skin is quite thin, but surprisingly strong and resistant to even a sharp knife. Seeds are small and dark blue, like little glass beads, and are found in groups of three in the skin nodules. The flesh is firm and has no distinctive texture. Its taste varies as you eat it and seems to include the flavours of every fruit you have ever tasted. As far as I am aware, this fruit has yet to be classified by botanists.

niseke – This term applies to those who have second sight or some other affinity with the world of spirits. It is also often applied to people who have unusual skills or knowledge, like herbalists or hunters who can imitate animal and bird calls so convincingly that they attract the animals to them. Witch doctors and other sorcerers are *niseke* and are treated with distinct respect and varying degrees of awe and fear. They generally live on the fringes of communities and many spend much of their time alone in the forest practising their esoteric arts.

nsia – A word with the same meaning and connotations as *niseke* (qv) but used in Mali in West Africa. Also a woman's name.

oukwe – This is a measure of liquid volume equal to just over two pints. An *akwali* (qv) with a capacity of 15 *oukwe* will hold about thirty-one pints of water when full to the shoulder.

pili-pili – A very small, very hot variety of pepper that grew in the forest. This was used in many of our sauces to enhance flavours and provide a bit of bite.

sabakwe – This is used as both a linear and an area measure. It is of no fixed dimension, being related directly to the size of an individual. As a linear measurement, one *sabakwe* is the equivalent of the person's height plus the circumference of his or her head. The area measurement is the same thing squared. *Sabakwe* is used as the traditional measure for land when it is sold or when a bride price is being set and is used to determine the size of houses and similar structures.

Our new village meeting house covered an area of 120 *sabakwe*. This measure was derived from the cumulative height and head circumference of the fifteen tallest men in the village for the length and of the eight tallest for the width. It gave us a finished building of approximately 116 feet long and 62 feet wide. For a forest community like Inkwiti, this was a very big structure.

Acknowledgements

A BOOK LIKE THIS DOESN'T write itself, however gripping the tale. Many people have contributed to bringing it to you in print and I am grateful to all of them in many different ways.

Firstly I am grateful to the people of Inkwiti, who accepted me into their lives, sharing their village, their forest and their wisdom freely and making me feel part of the community. Also in Zaïre, my thanks go to Mobutu Sese Seko for his friendship and for providing me access to areas and people that might otherwise have been denied; to Nkwanu Knaii, his family and the men of his MPR cadre, for taking me under their wings and teaching me the local ways and so much more.

I am grateful to Abélé for bringing sunshine to my house, for being a dutiful daughter and to Mputu Mngunko for finally taking her off my hands and being a good husband to her.

During the writing of this story, many people have helped, among them Mike and Jill Cable, who published my first book, read and advised on a lot of my writing and, with great patience, helped me present this story in a readable form. Helena Drysdale gave constructive editorial advice; Jane Brake, Jenny Simmonds and

Alan Carr read my manuscript and helped me iron out inconsistencies in my writing.

Many friends and family, too numerous to be named individually, have encouraged me to keep writing and given me the purpose to get this finished; their contribution cannot easily be measured but I am immensely grateful for it all the same.

My particular thanks go to my publisher, Chuck Grieve, and his team at Mosaïque Press, for believing in me, for working patiently over many months and having the courage to publish my work. Also for the many cups of excellent coffee which fuelled our discussions.

Lastly, and most importantly, special thanks must go to my wife, Gay, without whose years of patience putting up with me, persistence in keeping me alive and for the endless encouragement and support along the way this book would never have been written.